DANCING IN THE STREET

This book is dedicated to all music makers

DANCING IN THE STREET

A Poetry Party

thrown by
Adrian Mitchell

illustrated by
Tony Ross

 ORCHARD BOOKS

ORCHARD BOOKS
96 Leonard Street, London EC2A 4XD
Orchard Books, Australia
14 Mars Road, Lane Cove, NSW 2066
ISBN 1 86039 693 3
First published in Great Britain in 1999
Selection © Adrian Mitchell 1999
Illustrations © Tony Ross 1999
The rights of Adrian Mitchell to be identified
as the compiler and Tony Ross as the illustrator of this work
have been asserted by them in accordance with the
Copyright, Designs and Patents Act, 1988.
A CIP catalogue record for this book is available
from the British Library.
1 3 5 7 9 10 8 6 4 2
Printed in Great Britain

Contents

ZOO OF DREAMS

WELL IT'S SATURDAY NIGHT AND I JUST GOT PAID

RIVER DEEP MOUNTAIN HIGH

TEARS OF RAGE

SISTERS

THE FIRST TIME EVER I SAW YOUR FACE

THE PARTY'S OVER

Dancing in the Street

Calling out around the world are you ready for a brand-new beat?
Summer's here and the time is right for dancing in the street.
  They're dancing in Chicago
  Down in New Orleans
  In New York City
All we need is music, sweet music,
There'll be music everywhere.
There'll be swinging and swaying and records playing
And dancing in the street.

Oh, it doesn't matter what you wear
Just as long as you are there.
So come on, every guy, grab a girl.
Ev'rywhere around the world
They'll be dancing, they're dancing in the street.

This is an invitation across the nation a chance for folks to meet.
There'll be laughing singing and music swinging dancing in the street.
  Philadelphia PA
  Baltimore and DC
  Now can't forget the Motor City
All we need is music, sweet music,
There'll be music everywhere.
There'll be swinging and swaying and records playing
And dancing in the street.

Way down in LA ev'ry day they're dancing in the street.
Let's form a big strong line, get in time, dancing in the street.
Across the ocean blue, me and you, we're dancing in the street…

WILLIAM STEVENSON, MARVIN GAYE and IVY HUNTER

DANCING IN THE STREET

YOUR INVITATION

Her dark hair was flowing over her freckles. She stood barefoot on the beach in her turquoise dress. Then her brown arms swung, and the bat in her hand smashed the rounders ball, and also my heart, way into the distance . . .

That was the moment. I was fourteen and I fell desperately in love with her. We only saw each other for two weeks a year, on those seaside holidays in Devon. I never told her how I felt, I never even held her hand. But I loved her, silently, for four years. And I wrote 800 midnight poems for her, which I was ashamed to show to my dog Jumble. Poems in which I tried to understand what love was all about and why it was doing what it was doing to me.

At the same time I began to write poems in which I tried to understand what war was all about and why people killed each other. I had plenty of friends and even belonged to a loose gang at school whose rebellion took the form of writing and performing wild plays and poems. But I was, like all my friends, longing for real love.

We tried to learn about it from books. The best physical descriptions were mostly in disreputable novels, passed from hand to hand till they fell apart. But we knew there was more to love than bodies. The deeper feelings of love, hate, joy, grief and laughter were most intensely expressed in poems and songs.

So when I came to put together *Dancing in the Street* as an anthology of poems for teenagers today, I decided to throw a party – a party crowded with poems and songs. It would be wild and exciting and funny, but like all the best parties it would have its quieter and more thoughtful moments – in the kitchen or down the garden.

Poets from all centuries were invited. There were hundreds more I wanted to ask, but when a party's too big it gets way out of hand. There's no dress code or age limit at this party, but twelve or thirteen would be a good time to arrive. And – so long as you're enjoying the party – never, ever leave.

Is there really a need for yet another anthology? You bet. When I rifled through the Massed Anthologies on my shelves it seemed to me that many of them were trying to be the Country Diary of an Edwardian Gentlewoman set to verse. I wanted something altogether funkier. I wanted William Blake boozing with the ghosts of Teddy Boys in the brothels of Villon's Paris and the loser gangs of Bruce Springsteen zipping though space in their Nortons towards the Planet of the Lost Ranters.

So it's not a respectable anthology, mainly because I don't enjoy respectable parties. But I was told by good friends who are teachers that I must exclude very rude words or the book would be banned in many schools. I thought about this a lot. Some of the best modern poems swear like parrots. I gave in. Almost all teenagers have to go to school and they're the people I want to talk to. Therefore –

A NOTE FOR TEACHERS: THIS ANTHOLOGY
CONTAINS NO VERY RUDE WORDS.

(The teachers I know aren't worried by Language – but some Parents and Governors are.)

You'll have a good time if you enjoyed *The Orchard Book of Poems*, which I assembled for a younger age group – say from eight to infinity. I've left out almost all the poems which appeared there or in *The Rattle Bag*, which is a fine anthology, but less urban than this one, since it's edited by those Vocal Yokels Ted Hughes and Seamus Heaney. Read these three anthologies and you've more or less seen the universe.

Learn your favourite poems by heart. Sounds like work but it's more like a game. A poem in your heart can be really useful, whether you're lonely – at school, at work, in prison, in the army, on a desert island –

or whether you're with people you love and you want to share your feelings – in the pub, by the seaside, on a mountain or at a funeral or a wedding party. And if you can't find the poem you need in this collection – roll your own.

I've included the lyrics of many songs. Poetry started, in tribes, as something which was always sung and usually danced. In the last couple of centuries, in Britain anyway, most poetry experts have been snobbish about song lyrics. But I've invited – among others – vintage rock poets like Paul McCartney and Bruce Springsteen as well as new writers like Hugh Barker and Hank Starrs of the group Animals That Swim.

Of course there's a difference between writing a song and a poem. When you write a song you usually leave a little more room between the words for the music to do its work. And most song lyrics are written without any thought at all except the thought of making money. "What do the words matter?" I've often heard. "Nobody listens to the words."

Yes we do, is my reply. I've always tried to hear the words of songs, searching for good phrases, moving or funny lines. And I've met plenty of teenagers who keep books in which they write down the lyrics of their favourite singers and groups.

So I've mixed up the words of new and old songs with new and old poems and stuck a CD on the machine. We've got a street clear of cars, a houseful of people and a bath full of ice, cans, bottles and a frozen monster or two.

Welcome to the party.
Let the good times roll!

Adrian

peace

mission statements made
while lingering on the Stairs
and visions seen
by gazing out of the cracked
Landing Window

Freedom to Dream

He dreams of bougainvillea, scarlet cordium and croton
hurtling across the gardens of frangipani, mint and fuschia,

each bloom a parachute looming up and beyond the pasture
instead of down on the grassland below the rainbow hill;

he dreams of *in* as *out*, *under* as *above*, *round* as *straight*,
and so he sees amutjomh dreary and earnest as a carnival

of musicians and dancers, a procession of antic revellers;
but those old reveries reveal images of a difficult truth.

He dreams of mountains, twisty rivers and pinched streams
arcing past art-landscapes of deserts, plains and valleys,

and he makes of his earth-visions a mansion in the clouds
and decides to live in the folds of his dreams forever.

ANDREW SALKEY

Dreams

Here we are all, by day; by night we are hurled
By dreams, each one into a several world.

ROBERT HERRICK

Solstice Roundelay

In the cold ground a tree
in the bare tree a bird
in the shy bird a heart
in the warm heart a song
in the sweet song a life
in the brief life a flight

In the flight a brief life
in the life a sweet song
in the song a warm heart
in the heart a shy bird
in the bird a bare tree
in the tree a cold ground

In the cold ground a tree
in the bare tree a bird
in the shy bird a heart
in the warm heart a song
in the sweet song a life
in the brief life a flight

JEFF CLOVES

I'm a Rocker

I got a 007 watch and it's a one and only
It's got a I-Spy beeper that tells me when
  you're lonely
I got a Batmobile so I can reach ya' in a
  fast shake
When your world's in crisis of an
  impendin' heartbreak

Now don't you call James Bond or Secret
  Agent Man
Cause they can't do it, like I can
I'm a rocker, baby, I'm a rocker – every
  day
I'm a rocker, baby, I'm a rocker

If you're hanging from a cliff or you're tied
  to the tracks, girl
Colombo split and you can't find Kojak
True love is broken and your tears are
  fallin' faster
You're sufferin' from a pain in your heart
  or some other natural disaster

Now I don't care what kind of shape
  you're in
If they put up a roadblock, I'll parachute in

I'm a rocker, baby, I'm a rocker – I'm in
       love
I'm a rocker, baby, I'm a rocker – every
       day
I'm a rocker, baby, I'm a rocker – with you

So you fell for some jerk who was tall,
       dark and handsome
Then he kidnapped your heart and now
       he's holdin' it for ransom
Well, like a mission impossible I'm gonna
       go and get it back
You know I would'a taken better care of it,
       baby, than that

Sometimes I get so hot, girl, well, I can't
       talk
But when I'm with you I cool off, and I walk
I'm a rocker, baby, I'm a rocker, and I talk
I'm a rocker, baby, I'm a rocker, every day
I'm a rocker, baby, I'm a rocker, every day

BRUCE SPRINGSTEEN

How Water Began to Play

Water wanted to live
It went to the sun it came weeping back
Water wanted to live
It went to the trees they burned it came weeping back
They rotted it came weeping back
Water wanted to live
It went to the flowers they crumpled it came weeping back
It wanted to live
It went to the womb it met blood
It came weeping back
It went to the womb it met knife
It came weeping back
It went to the womb it met maggot and rottenness
It came weeping back it wanted to die

It went to time it went through the stone door
It came weeping back
It went searching through all space for nothingness
It came weeping back it wanted to die

Till it had no weeping left

It lay at the bottom of all things

Utterly worn out   utterly clear

TED HUGHES

The Coming of Good Luck

So Good Luck came, and on my roof did light,
Like noiseless snow; or as the dew of night:
Not all at once, but gently, as the trees
Are, by the sunbeams, tickled by degrees.

ROBERT HERRICK

The Waking

I wake to sleep, and take my waking slow.
I feel my fate in what I cannot fear.
I learn by going where I have to go.

We think by feeling. What is there to know?
I hear my being dance from ear to ear.
I wake to sleep, and take my waking slow.

Of those so close beside me, which are you?
God bless the Ground! I shall walk softly there,
And learn by going where I have to go.

Light takes the Tree; but who can tell us how?
The lowly worm climbs up a winding stair;
I wake to sleep, and take my waking slow.

Great Nature has another thing to do
To you and me; so take the lively air,
And, lovely, learn by going where to go.

This shaking keeps me steady. I should know.
What falls away is always. And is near.
I wake to sleep, and take my waking slow.
I learn by going where I have to go.

THEODORE ROETHKE

Ode to the Tomato

The street
drowns in tomatoes:
noon,
summer,
light
breaks
in two
tomato
halves,
and the streets
run
with juice.
In December
the tomato
cuts loose,
invades
kitchens,
takes over lunches,
settles
at rest
on sideboards,
with the glasses,

butter dishes,
blue salt-cellars.
It has
its own radiance,
a goodly majesty.
Too bad we must
assassinate:
a knife
plunges
into its living pulp,
red
viscera,
a fresh,
deep,
inexhaustible
sun
floods the salads
of Chile,
beds cheerfully
with the blonde onion,
and to celebrate
oil
the filial essence
of the olive tree
lets itself fall
over its gaping hemispheres,
the pimento
adds
its fragrance,
salt its magnetism –
we have the day's
wedding:

parsley
flaunts
its little flags,
potatoes
thump to a boil,
the roasts
beat
down the door
with their aromas:
it's time!
let's go!
and upon
the table,
belted by summer,
tomatoes,
stars of the earth,
stars multiplied
and fertile
show off
their convolutions,
canals
and plenitudes
and the abundance
boneless,
without husk,
or scale or thorn,
grant us
the festival
of ardent colour
and all-embracing freshness.

PABLO NERUDA

I Started Early – Took My Dog –

I started Early – Took my Dog –
And visited the Sea –
The Mermaids in the Basement
Came out to look at me –

And Frigates – in the Upper Floor
Extended Hempen Hands –
Presuming Me to be a Mouse –
Aground – upon the Sands –

But no Man moved Me – till the Tide
Went past my simple Shoe –
And past my Apron – and my Belt
And past my Bodice – too –

And made as He would eat me up –
As wholly as a Dew
Upon a Dandelion's Sleeve –
And then – I started – too –

And He – He followed – close behind –
I felt His Silver Heel
Upon my Ankle – Then my Shoes
Would overflow with Pearl –

Until We met the Solid Town –
No One He seemed to know –
And bowing – with a Mighty look –
At me – The Sea withdrew –

EMILY DICKINSON

I Know Moonlight

I know moonlight,
I know starlight,
I lay this body down.

I walk in the moonlight,
I walk in the starlight,
I lay this body down.

I go to judgement
In the evenin' of the day,
When I lay this body down.

ANON

Prelude

Still south I went and west and south again,
Through Wicklow from the morning till the night,
And far from cities, and the sites of men,
Lived with the sunshine and the moon's delight.

I know the stars, the flowers, and the birds,
The grey and wintry sides of many glens,
And did but half remember human words,
In converse with the mountains, moors and fens.

J. M. SYNGE

Inattention

A child sitting on a doorstep looks up from his book.
In the room behind him a woman is writing a letter.
On the waste land across the street from him
a gasometer casts its shadow over a solitary lilac.

Like an animal grazing over grass
he has been grazing over words,
stopping at the familiar, the wondrous.
Over and over, as if it were a spell, he repeats the word *cargo*.

Out on an ocean phosphite clings to rusting propellers,
whales rise like islands, rain falls into nothing.
The shadow from the gasometer creeps beyond the lilac,
over the bindweed, the sweet-scented camomiles, the stray
          thistles.

And now the child has abandoned his book.
He has become the captain of a great ship and its cargo of
          treasure.
Sailors who've lost their sight report to him
on how the stars have vanished.

In the house behind him a woman is packing belongings.
Another book, an encyclopedia of regrets, is banished to its
          own space.
The shadow from the gasometer creeps on; a slow,
          irrevocable flood.
It leaves behind the lilac, the bindweed, the sweet-scented
          camomiles.

BRIAN PATTEN

Dinner Tickets

My mother always looked
For dinner tickets
In the breast pocket
Of my grey school shirt.

Dried mud
Falls from my workboots.
Zig zag sculptures
Leave a trail as I head
For the woods.

She found a folded drawing
Of a naked woman.
My father asked me about it.

Chainsaw makes easy work
Of young birch blocking my path.

For days I denied all knowledge
Of the shocking work of art.

Resting on a fallen log,
I wipe the sweat from my brow.

Finally admitting
I had made
The drawing,
I cried.

PAUL MCCARTNEY

I Stepped from Plank to Plank

I stepped from Plank to Plank
A slow and cautious way
The Stars about my Head I felt
About my Feet the Sea.

I knew not but the next
Would be my final inch –
This gave me that precarious Gait
Some call Experience.

EMILY DICKINSON

Leaps of Feeling

There's nothing like a party. Nothing.
        Last night
another dream. The swinging roomful
of zodiac signs.
Showplace of trends and flair.
A piece of spectacle – everybody.
Steps unknown rush in and dance you.

Nothing like a party.
Food isn't for table.
Music's a crowd's own age.
Joy of a drink is the slow sweaty sip.
Wit is how it shoots down brilliance.
Malice of a gossip is how
it is spiced up.

Nothing like a party.
A known voice shatters you.
A known hug collects you up.
A new squeeze charges like champagne.
All dream girls. All show blokes.
Dazzlers rave up those who
only manage a glimmer.
To be, you become
a room of pleasure-pulsing.

Nothing like a party. Nothing.
Reality isn't big enough.
Wishes die.
But hopes mount like flames.
Mixes push somebody
here and there over the top.
It's a night of clusters:
it works leaps of feeling.
Just can't find where else
I'm more discovered.

JAMES BERRY

TAKE IT TO THE LIMIT

tall and low-down stories of
    heroes and villains
told in the Living and
    Partly Living Room
with flashing lights
and thumping music

The Ballad of Jesse James

Jesse James was a lad that killed many-a man,
He robbed the Glendale train;
But that dirty little coward that shot Mr Howard,
Has laid poor Jesse in his grave.

Jesse had a wife to mourn all her life,
The children they are brave.
'Twas a dirty little coward shot Mister Howard,
And laid Jesse James in his grave.

It was his brother Frank who robbed the Gallatin bank
And carried the money from the town;
It was in this very place that they had a little race
For they shot Captain Sheets to the ground.

Jesse had a wife to mourn all her life,
The children they are brave.
'Twas a dirty little coward shot Mister Howard,
And laid Jesse James in his grave.

They went to the crossing not very far from there
And there they did the same;
And the agent on his knees he delivered up the keys
To the outlaws Frank and Jesse James.

Jesse had a wife to mourn all her life,
The children they are brave.
'Twas a dirty little coward shot Mister Howard,
And laid Jesse James in his grave.

It was on a Wednesday night, the moon was shining bright,
They robbed the Glendale train.
And the people they did say, for many miles away,
'Twas the outlaws Frank and Jesse James.

Jesse had a wife to mourn all her life,
The children they are brave.
'Twas a dirty little coward shot Mister Howard,
And laid Jesse James in his grave.

It was on a Saturday night, Jesse was at home
Talking to his family brave,
Robert Ford came along like a thief in the night
And laid poor Jesse in his grave.

Jesse had a wife to mourn all her life,
The children they are brave.
'Twas a dirty little coward shot Mister Howard,
And laid Jesse James in his grave.

How people held their breath when they heard of Jesse's death
And wondered how he ever came to die.
It was one of the gang, little Robert Ford,
He shot poor Jesse on the sly.

Jesse had a wife to mourn all her life,
The children they are brave.
'Twas a dirty little coward shot Mister Howard,
And laid Jesse James in his grave.

Yes it was Robert Ford, the dirty little coward,
I wonder how he does feel,
For he ate of Jesse's bread and he slept in Jesse's bed,
Then he laid poor Jesse in his grave.

Jesse had a wife to mourn all her life,
The children they are brave.
'Twas a dirty little coward shot Mister Howard,
And laid Jesse James in his grave.

Jesse went to his rest with his hand upon his breast,
The Devil's own smile on his face.
He was born one day in the County of Clay
And he came of a solitary race.

Jesse had a wife to mourn all her life,
The children they are brave.
'Twas a dirty little coward shot Mister Howard,
And laid Jesse James in his grave.

ANON

NOTE: 'Mister Howard' was the name Jesse James used when he was hiding.

34

Frontier Story

Meanwhile, back at the ranch factory
they were turning out whole stampedes
just for the hell of it, the mile-long door slid back
and they reverted to dust at the first touch of air.
But the music of the dust flowed back over the assembly-line
and that was the Christmas of a thousand million cowboys.

Steers went lowing upland, purple sage country
with boots on marched west out back as
bulldozers like mobile capital cities
trunched up dead million-bed motels and charged
some gaily eroded buttes with simulating cowboys.

The diggers were worse than any sands of the sea
and dynamite only loosened myriads off sideways
till a bag of megatons went critical and
there were horses' eyeholes all over the Coalsack
and when we came in we were crunching through cowboys.

Or so we were told as we laid Los Angeles on Boston
and took a few states out, we were only playing,
pulled Mexico up over us and went to sleep,
woke up spitting out Phoenicians into the Cassiterides
and gave a yawn a wave as it flew out full of cowboys.

They sat in our teeth with red-hot spurs and I said
'Back to the drawing-board', but the belt was humming
and pushed the continuum into funky gopher-holes
with a prime number down each hole wheezing
so cheekily we had to make more cowboys

first. Meanwhile, back at the ranch
factory they were diligently making
us, just for the hell of it, the mile-long door
slid back and we reverted to dust at the touch
of air. But our music lingers in the bones of cowboys.

EDWIN MORGAN

Robinson Crusoe

Chapter One

In the evening they ate their soup and went to smoke their pipes
beside the sea. The smell of their tobacco made the fishes cough.
Robinson Crusoe was not enjoying himself on the desert island.
"It's really too deserted," he said. His Man Friday agreed with him.
He said to his good master: "Yes, Master, a desert island is much
too deserted." And he shook his great black head.
The End.

ERIK SATIE

Barbara Allen

In Scarlet town, where I was born,
There was a fair maid dwelling,
Made every youth cry "Well aday!"
Her name was Barbara Allen.

All in the merry month of May,
When green buds they are swelling,
Young Jimmy Green on his death bed lay
For the love of Barbara Allen.

He sent his man unto her there,
To the town where she was dwelling;
"O you must come to my master dear,
If your name be Barbara Allen.

"For death is printed on his face
And o'er his heart is stealing;
O haste away to comfort him,
O lovely Barbara Allen!"

"If death is printed on his face
And o'er his heart is stealing,
Yet little better shall he be
For the love of Barbara Allen."

So, slowly, slowly, she came up,
And slowly she came nigh him;
And all she said when there she came,
"Young man, I think you're dying."

He turned his face unto her straight,
With deadly sorrow sighing:
"O lovely maid, come pity me!
I'm on my death bed lying."

"If on your death bed you do lie,
What need the tale you're telling?
I cannot keep you from your death:
Farewell," said Barbara Allen.

He turned his face unto the wall,
And deadly pains he fell in:
"Adieu, adieu, adieu to all,
Adieu to Barbara Allen."

As she was walking o'er the fields,
She heard the bell a-knelling;
And every stroke it seemed to say,
"Unworthy Barbara Allen."

She turned herself around about
And spied the corpse a-coming:
"Lay down, lay down the corpse," said she,
"That I may look upon him."

With scornful eyes she did look down,
Her cheeks with laughter swelling;
While all her friends cried out amen,
"Unworthy Barbara Allen!"

When he was dead and laid in grave,
Her heart was struck with sorrow:
"O mother, mother, make my bed,
For I shall die to-morrow.

"Hard-hearted creature him to slight,
He who loved me so dearly!
O had I been more kind to him,
When he was alive and near me!"

On her death bed as she did lay,
She begged to be buried by him,
And sorely repented of that day
That she e'er did deny him.

"Farewell, ye virgins all," she said,
"And shun the fault I've fell in;
Henceforward take warning by the fall
Of cruel Barbara Allen."

One was buried in the high churchyard,
The other in the choir;
On one there grew a red rose bush,
On the other there grew a brier.

They grew and they grew to the high steeple top,
Till they could grow no higher;
And there they locked in a true-lover's knot,
For true lovers to admire.

ANON

The Australian Poem

A sunburnt bloody stockman stood,
And in a dismal bloody mood
Apostrophized his bloody cuddy:
"This bloody moke's no bloody good,
He doesn't earn his bloody food,
Bloody, bloody, bloody."

He leapt upon his bloody horse
And galloped off of bloody course.
The road was wet and bloody muddy,
It led him to the bloody creek.
The bloody horse was bloody weak.
Bloody, bloody, bloody.

He said: "This bloody steed must swim,
The same for me as bloody him."
The creek was deep and bloody floody,
So ere they reached the bloody bank
The bloody steed beneath him sank,
The stockman's face a bloody study,
Ejaculating bloody, bloody, bloody.

ANON

Jake's Amazing Suit

When you see me in my suit –
You'll look and at first
All you'll see is a burst
Of shimmering electric blue.
Then you'll focus in and see
That the vision is me
And I'm walking
And my suit is walking too

When you see me in my suit –
Flowing soft as milk
It'll be Thailand silk
That follows any move at all.
And its cut and its drape
Will lay on me a shape
Like I'm standing
Underneath a waterfall.

When you see me in my suit –
I won't be able to walk out in public
Because of my wonderful threads
Never mind, instead,
We'll spend our life in bed
With nothing but love in our heads
When you see me in my suit!

I once saw Miles Davis
Walk across the tarmac from an aeroplane.
Yes I once saw Miles Davis walking
Oh now let me explain –

His face was carved from a living mahogany tree-trunk.
He wore power sunglasses over his eyes
With silver pistons connected to his ears.
His beret sat on the top of his head
Like a little powder-blue cloud
And when he smiled it turned you to stone.

His suit was four and a half times too big for his body.
It was kind of a tweed woven out of mountain light.
It had criss-cross lines of the sort of luminous
Green you only see on the top of birthday cakes.
And the luminous green lines
Criss-crossed over a meadow of bright creamy white

I once saw Miles Davis
Walk across the tarmac from an aeroplane
Yes I once saw Miles Davis walking
I can explain –

I want a suit like that
I want a suit like that
I want a suit so electric
If I leave it alone
It'll jump off the hanger
Take a walk on its own
Give me a suit like that

Give me a suit like that
So that my love will love me
Even more than she loves me
When she sees me in my suit
When she sees me in my suit

ADRIAN MITCHELL

The Great Staircase

It's a huge staircase, really enormous.
It has more than a thousand steps,
All made of ivory.
It is very beautiful.
Nobody dares use it for fear of spoiling it.
The King himself has never used it.
To leave his room, he jumps out of the window.
He often says to himself:
I love this staircase so much
I'm going to have it wrapped in straw.

Isn't the King right?

ERIK SATIE

Velvet Wave

The velvet inside
a guitar case
Set the strings
Giddy humming to
the silver vibration of a note

A quick flowing
Stream by the roadside
Buzzed towards the seaside
Tattoos and Torture Tents
Along the shingle shore

Thin echoes of headphones
Ride the murky old bass
Screaming feedback
At the fat lady bather

A wave flaps in on itself

PAUL MCCARTNEY

The Preacher Tells a Story at the Graveside

He wasn't rich and he wasn't clever.
His voice was quiet. He found words difficult.
He used to come into church as if somebody might hit him
And always, in public, he kept his right hand in his pocket.

When war broke out, we called up the young men.
They were weighed and measured and questioned – then they signed.
I sat beside the Captain.
The room was crowded with fathers.
Outside on the grass the young men were fooling about and laughing.

Then this young man stepped forward,
White as the snow at the edge of a glacier.
"Come closer," said the Captain. "Closer."
The young man rested his right hand on the table – it was wrapped
    in bandages.
The young man mumbled something – how his sickle had slipped
By accident and cut his finger off, by accident.

There was no sound at all in the room.
Then the Captain stood up. He was as grey as steel.
And "Get out," the Captain said. "Get out."

So the young man got out, but it took a long time.
Fathers fell back on either side, and they stared and stared
As he walked the gauntlet between them
Until, eventually, he reached the door and ran
Out of the town up to his home in the mountains.
He leased a farm. He married. He built a house.
He broke up the hard ground. He managed well.

The small fields of his farm swayed with golden crops.
His first farm was destroyed by a flood.
He started again, created another farm.
His second farm was crushed by an avalanche.
He started again, his house rose again for the third time.

He and his wife had three sons, bright as buttons.
But their school was reached by a mountain path
Beside a terrifying ravine.
So the man tied himself to his eldest son,
And he carried the youngest son in his arms,
And he carried the other son on his back.
For years he struggled them through to school,
And they grew to be men, and they went to America,
And they became rich, and they forgot their father.

He was a short-sighted man.
He only talked to those who were close to him.
To him the rousing speeches of patriotic leaders
Were as meaningless as the music of cowbells.
But he was humble, this old man with nine fingers was humble.
In the eyes of the state, he was a bad citizen perhaps,
But in the little country of his family –
There he was a great man. There he was himself.

So, peace be with you.
You fought bravely in the war all farmers fight.
I hope that today you stand before God
And He smiles as you take your right hand out of your pocket
And your right hand is whole again.

HENRIK IBSEN

The Promised Land

I left my home in Norfolk, Virginia,
California on my mind
I straddled that Greyhound and rode him into Raleigh
And on across Caroline.
We stopped at Charlotte, we by-passed Rock Hill,
We never was a minute late;
We was ninety miles out of Atlanta by sundown
Rollin' out of Georgia state.
We had motor trouble that turned into a struggle
Halfway across Alabam
And that 'Hound broke down and left us all stranded
In Downtown Birmingham.

Right away I bought me a through train ticket
Right across Mississippi clean,
And I was on the Midnight Flyer out of Birmingham
Smokin' into New Orleans.
Somebody helped me get out of Louisiana
Just to help me to get to Houston Town.
There are people there who care a little 'bout me
And they won't let a poor boy down.
Sure as you're born they bought me a silk suit
They put luggage in my hand
And I woke up high over Albuquerque
On a jet to the Promised Land.

Workin' on a T-bone steak I had a party
Flyin' over to the Golden State
When the pilot told us in thirteen minutes

He would get us at the Terminal Gate.
Swing low, chariot, come down easy,
Taxi to the Terminal Zone
Cut your engines and cool your wings
And let me make it to the telephone.
Los Angeles, give me Norfolk, Virginia,
Tidewater 4-0-9.
Tell the folks back home this is the Promised Land callin'
And the poor boy's on the line.

CHUCK BERRY

ZOO OF DREAMS

featuring some creatures who lurk
down the end of the Garden Jungle
among the damp hutches
for rabbits and dragons

Every Living Creature

And now the Beasts are walking from the wood,
As well of Ravine, as that chew the Cud,
The King of Beasts his fury doth suppresse,
And to the Arke leads downe the Lionesse,
The Bull for his beloved mate doth low,
And to the Arke brings on the faire ey'd Cow;
The stately Courser for his Mare doth nay,
And t'wards the new Arke guideth her the way;
The wreath'd-horn'd Ram his safety doth pursue,
And to the Arke ushers his gentle Ewe;
The bristly Boare, who with his snowte up plow'd
The spacious Plaines, and with his grunting lowd,
Rais'd ratling Ecchoes all the Woods about,
Leaves his dark Den, and having scented out
Noah's new-built Arke, in with his Sow doth come,
And stye themselves up in a little roome:
The Hart with his deare Hind, the Buck and Doe,
Leaving their wildnesse, bring the tripping Roe
Along with them: and from the Mountaine steepe,
The clambring Goat, and Cony, us'd to keepe
Amongst the Cleeves, together get, and they
To this great Arke finde out the ready way;
Th'unweildy Elke, whose skin is of much proofe,
Throngs with the rest t'attaine this wooden roofe;
The Unicorne leaves off his pride, and closse
There sets him downe by the Rhinoceros:
The Elephant there comming to imbarque,
And as he softly getteth up the Arke,
Feeling by his great waight, his body sunck,

Holds by his huge Tooth, and his nervy Trunck;
The croock-backt Camel climing to the deck,
Drawes up himselfe with his long sinewy neck;
The spotted Panther whose delicious scent,
Oft causeth beasts his harbor to frequent,
But having got them once into his power,
Sucketh their blood, and doth their flesh devoure,
His cruelty hath quickly cast aside,
And waxing courteous, doth become their guide,
And brings into this universall Shop
The Ounce, the Tigar, and the Antilop,
By the grim Woolfe, the poore Sheepe safely lay,
And was his care, which lately was his pray;
The Asse upon the Lyon leant his head,
And to the Cat the Mouse for succour fled;
The silly Hare doth cast aside her feare,
And formes her selfe fast by the ugly Beare,
At whom the watchfull Dog did never barke,
When he espyde him clambring up the Arke:
The Fox got in, his subtilties hath left,
And as ashamed of his former theft,
Sadly sits there as though he did repent,
And in the Arke became an innocent:
The fine-furd Ermin, Martern, and the Cat
That voydeth Civet, there together sat
By the shrewd Muncky, Babian, and the Ape,
With the Hienna, much their like in shape,
Which by their kinde, are ever doing ill,
Yet in the Arke, sit civilly and still;

The skipping Squerrill of the Forrest free,
That leapt so nimbly betwixt tree and tree,
It selfe into the Arke then nimbly cast,
As 'twere a Ship-boy come to clime the Mast.

MICHAEL DRAYTON

The Ants

What wonder strikes the curious, while he views
    The black ant's city, by a rotten tree
Or woodland bank! In ignorance we muse:
    Pausing, annoy'd, we know not what we see,
    Such government and thought there seem to be;
Some looking on, and urging some to toil,
    Dragging their loads of bent-stalks slavishly;
And what's more wonderful, when big loads foil
One ant or two to carry, quickly then
A swarm flock round to help their fellow-men.
    Surely they speak a language whisperingly,
Too fine for us to hear; and sure their ways
    Prove they have kings and laws, and they be
Deformed remnants of the fairy-days.

JOHN CLARE

52

Dog Show

I dreamed I was a dog in a dog show.
And my father came to the dog show.
And he said: That's a really good dog.
I like that dog.

And then all my friends came and I
was thinking:
No one has ever looked at me like this
for so long.
No one has ever stared at me like this
for so long
for such a long time
for so long.

LAURIE ANDERSON

The Mosquito Knows

The mosquito knows full well, small as he is
he's a beast of prey.
But after all
he only takes his bellyful,
he doesn't put my blood in the bank.

D. H. LAWRENCE

Calico Pie

Calico Pie,
The little Birds fly
Down to the calico tree,
Their wings were blue,
And they sang "Tilly-loo!"
Till away they flew, –
And they never came back to me!
They never came back!
They never came back!
They never came back to me!

Calico Jam
The little Fish swam,
Over the syllabub sea,
He took off his hat,
To the Sole and the Sprat,
And the Willeby-wat, –
But he never came back to me!
He never came back!
He never came back!
He never came back to me!

Calico Ban,
The little Mice ran,
To be ready in time for tea,
Flippity flup,
They drank it all up,
And danced in the cup, –
But they never came back to me!

They never came back!
They never came back!
They never came back to me!

Calico Drum,
The Grasshoppers come,
The Butterfly, Beetle, and Bee,
Over the ground,
Around and round,
With a hop and a bound, –
But they never came back!
They never came back!
They never came back!
They never came back to me!

EDWARD LEAR

The Lake

For years there have been no fish in the lake.
People hurrying through the park avoid it like the plague.
Birds steer clear and the sedge of course has withered.
Trees lean away from it, and at night it reflects,
not the moon, but the blackness of its own depths.
There are no fish in the lake. But there is life there.
There is life…

Underwater pigs glide between reefs of coral debris.
They love it here. They breed and multiply
in sties hollowed out of the mud
and lined with mattresses and bedsprings.
They live on dead fish and rotting things,
drowned pets, plastic and assorted excreta.
Rusty cans they like the best.
Holding them in webbed trotters
their teeth tear easily through the tin
and poking in a snout
they noisily suck out
the putrid matter within.

There are no fish in the lake. But there is life there.
There is life…

For on certain evenings after dark
shoals of pigs surface and look out
at those houses near the park.
Where, in bathrooms, children feed stale bread to plastic ducks
and in attics, toy yachts have long since run aground.

Where, in living rooms, anglers dangle their lines
on patterned carpets, and bemoan the fate
of the ones that got away.

Down on the lake, piggy eyes glisten.
They have acquired a taste for flesh.
They are licking their lips. Listen…

ROGER MCGOUGH

Trouble Is

Rabbit running in circles
chasing his tail because
it looks like candy floss.
Trouble is – rabbits don't eat candy floss.

Black labrador barking at the antics
of his own shadow on a wall.
Trouble is – shadows don't fight back.

A pair of gloves hanging from
a back pocket argue about
which hand will hold the rake.
Trouble is – gloves don't give a shit.

PAUL MCCARTNEY

The Marvellous Bear Shepherd

There were two men of holy will
Who lived together without an ill,
All lonely in a hermitage,
As meek as birdes in a cage.
The one was called Eutucylus
The other hight Florentius.
Eutucylus he was the clerke
He taught the people Goddes werk.
Florens he had much less of lore,
But in prayer wrought ever more.
Beside the house an abbey lie
Whereat in time the abbot die.
Then alle the monks took them to rede
To choose who should reign in his stede,
And chose for them Eutucylus
To be the abbot of their house.
Upon all hands fell the lot
So Eutucylus was made abbot.
When he was gone Florens gan dwell
Lonely and wistful in his cell;
Withouten brother he made moan
For that he should dwell alone,
And had great sorrow and was dreary
As be they who lose good company.
And prayed he Gode, that he would have
Some good comforte of His love.
Thus prayed Florens by his bede
The Gode should send hym felauhede.
Thus prayed Florens by his bede

He prayed dere Gode of Hym take hede
And rising up and looking out
He saw a bere, wild and stout.
This bere he came unto the gate
He came to where Florens he sate,
And when the bere he came him nere
The bere him louted and made fair cheer;
Such fair cheer as a bere might make
And asked meek he would him take.
At this Florens him bethought
That God had heard what he besought
And thanked him of his sweet grace
That he had sent him such solace,
For a miracle he must understand
That a wild bere came so tame to hand.
Now Florens he had six sheep
But no herdsmen them to keep,
So bade the bere that he should go
And drive his sheepe to and fro.
"And kepe them well that none them tear
And thou shalt be my goode bere."
The bere him louted with semblence glad
For to do what Florens bade,
So to the bere he gave advice:
"Every day when I eat twice
Come thou home at high undurne
And no longer in the field sojourne!
And every day when I fast
At the nones come home at last."

So did the bere every day,
Nere one hour past he away,
But came he home unto the cell
Always at both times he knew well.
Then Florens had comfort and gain
Of his bere that was so tame,
And loved him much withouten fail
For the miracle and the mervaile;
      And, sooth to say, to him appeared
The bere was a most marvellous herd.
A bere through kinde should ete sheep
Yet here as herd he did them keep,
And the miracle might not be hid
The whole country knew it was did
That Florens had a tame bere
That of his sheep the herdsman were.

The Abbot that was Eutucylus
Had four disciples envious
That all day of this bere they spake,
With deep intent evil to make,
And said all four of them between
That it was great evil scorne and mean;
"More mervail did Florentius
Than doth our abbot Eutucylus,"
They said "that it shall not go so,"
And made forward that bere to slo.
As they said, so evil wrought,
And the dere bere to death they brought.

At evening time the bere came not.
Florens had thereof much thought
He rose and sped him to the field
And after his bere faste behelde,
And at last his bere he found,
Beside his sheep, slain, on the ground.

Then had Florens wroth and wo,
To know of evil that was so,
And plained him sore for his own dere
That they had slain his goode bere.
Hopeless he plained him wondrous sore,
That his solace was no more.
Of Jesu Christ had they no dread
That they should do this evil deed?
"My gentle Bere of goode will!
He ne'er did no man any ill.
He was sent to me of God's grace,
To be my help and my solace,
That God should send him me for love,
And they'd not suffer him to live."

Almighty God shall do his will,
On them and all who did this ill.
And above the earth they soon were stinking
That to the bere's death were consenting.

ANON

Mooses

The goofy Moose, the walking house-frame,
Is lost
In the forest. He bumps, he blunders, he stands.

With massy bony thoughts sticking out near his ears –
Reaching out palm upwards, to catch whatever
        might be falling from heaven –
He tries to think,
Leaning their huge weight
On the lectern of his front legs.

He can't find the world!
Where did it go? What does a world look like?
The Moose
Crashes on, and crashes into a lake, and stares at
        the mountain and cries:
"Where do I belong? This is no place!"

He turns dragging half the lake out after him
And charges the cackling underbrush –

He meets another Moose
He stares, he thinks: "It's only a mirror!"
"Where is the world?" he groans. "O my lost world!
And why am I so ugly?
And why am I so far away from my feet?"

He weeps.

Hopeless drops drip from his droopy lips.

The other Moose just stands there doing the same.

Two dopes of the deep woods.

TED HUGHES

The Skylark

The rolls and harrows lie at rest beside
The battered road; and spreading far and wide
Above the russet clods, the corn is seen
Sprouting its spiry points of tender green,
Where squats the hare, to terrors wide awake,
Like some brown clod the harrows failed to break.
Opening their golden caskets to the sun,
The buttercups make schoolboys eager run,
To see who shall be first to pluck the prize –
Up from their hurry, see, the skylark flies,
And o'er her half-formed nest, with happy wings
Winnows the air, till in the cloud she sings,
Then hangs a dust-spot in the sunny skies,
And drops, and drops, till in her nest she lies,
Which they unheeded passed – not dreaming then
That birds which flew so high would drop agen
To nests upon the ground, which anything
May come at to destroy. Had they the wing
Like such a bird, themselves would be too proud,
And build on nothing but a passing cloud!
As free from danger as the heavens are free
From pain and toil, there would they build and be,
And sail about the world to scenes unheard
Of and unseen – Oh, were they but a bird!
So think they, while they listen to its song,
And smile and fancy and so pass along;
While its low nest, moist with the dews of morn,
Lies safely, with the leveret, in the corn.

JOHN CLARE

Queen Kong

I remember peeping in at his skyscraper room
and seeing him fast asleep. My little man.
I'd been in Manhattan a week,
making my plans; staying at 2 quiet hotels
in the Village, where people were used to strangers
and more or less left you alone. To this day,
I'm especially fond of pastrami on rye.

I digress. As you see, this island's a paradise.
He'd arrived, my man, with a documentary team
to make a film. (There's a particular toad
that lays its eggs only here.) I found him alone
in a clearing, scooped him up in my palm,
and held his wriggling, shouting life till he calmed.
For me, it was absolutely love at first sight.

I'd been so *lonely*. Long nights in the heat
of my own pelt, rumbling an animal blues.
All right, he was small, but perfectly formed
and *gorgeous*. There were things he could do
for me with the sweet finesse of those hands
that no gorilla could. I swore in my huge heart
to follow him then to the ends of the earth.

For he wouldn't stay here. He was nervous.
I'd go to his camp each night at dusk,
crouch by the delicate tents, and wait.
          His colleagues
always sent him out pretty quick. He'd climb

into my open hand, sit down; and then
      I'd gently pick
at his shirt and his trews, peel him, put
the tip of my tongue to the grape of his flesh.

Bliss. But when he'd finished his prize-winning film,
he packed his case; hopped up and down
on my heartline, miming the flight back home
to New York. *Big metal bird.* Didn't he know
I could swat his plane from these skies like a gnat?
But I let him go, my man. I watched him fly
into the sun as I thumped at my breast, distraught.

I lasted a month. I slept for a week,
then woke to binge for a fortnight. I didn't wash.
The parrots clacked their migraine chant.
The swinging monkeys whinged.
      Fevered, I drank
handfuls of river right by the spot where he'd bathed.
I bled when a fat, red moon rolled on the jungle roof.
And after that, I decided to get him back.

So I came to sail up the Hudson one June night,
with the New York skyline a concrete rain-forest
of light; and felt, lovesick and vast, the first
glimmer of hope in weeks. I was discreet, prowled
those streets in darkness; pressing my passionate eye
to a thousand windows, each with its modest peep-show
of boredom or pain, of drama, consolation, remorse.
I found him, of course. At 3am on a Sunday,
dreaming alone in his single bed; over his lovely head,

a blown-up photograph of myself. I stared for a long time
till my big brown eyes grew moist, then I padded away
through Central Park, under the stars. He was mine.
Next day, I shopped. Clothes for my man, mainly,
but one or two treats for myself from Bloomingdales.

I picked him, like a chocolate from the top layer
of a box, one Friday night, out of his room;
and let him dangle in the air between my finger
and my thumb in a teasing, lover's way.
            Then we sat
on the tip of the Empire State Building, saying farewell
to the Brooklyn Bridge, to the winking yellow cabs,
to the helicopters over the river, dragonflies.

Twelve happy years. He slept in my fur; woke early
to massage the heavy lids of my eyes. I liked that.
He liked me to gently blow on him; or scratch,
with care, the length of his back with my nail.
Then I'd ask him to play on the wooden pipes he made
in our first year. He'd sit, cross-legged, near my ear
for hours; his plaintive, lost tunes making me cry.

When he died, I held him all night, shaking him
like a doll, licking his face, breast, soles of his feet,
his little rod. But then, heartsore as I was, I set to work.
He would be pleased. I wear him now about my neck,
perfect, preserved, with tiny emeralds for eyes. No man
has been loved more. I'm sure that, sometimes, in his silent death,
against my massive, breathing lungs, he hears me roar.

CAROL ANN DUFFY

The Kraken

Below the thunders of the upper deep;
Far, far beneath in the abysmal sea,
His ancient, dreamless, uninvaded sleep
The Kraken sleepeth; faintest sunlights flee
About his shadowy sides: above him swell
Huge sponges of millennial growth and height;
And far away into the sickly light,
From many a wondrous grot and secret cell
Unnumber'd and enormous polypi
Winnow with giant arms the slumbering green.
There hath he lain for ages and will lie
Battening upon huge seaworms in his sleep,
Until the latter fire shall heat the deep;
Then once by man and angels to be seen.
In roaring he shall rise and on the surface die.

ALFRED, LORD TENNYSON

WELL IT'S SATURDAY NIGHT AND I JUST GOT PAID

rumours of walks on the wild side
confided in corners of
    the Whispering Kitchen
where you can get anything you want –
except food

The Ballad of Villon and Fat Madge

"Tis no sin for a man to labour in his vocation."
"The night cometh, when no man can work."

What though the beauty I love and serve be cheap,
Ought you to take me for a beast or fool?
All things a man could wish are in her keep;
For her I turn swashbuckler in love's school.
When folk drop in, I take my pot and stool
And fall to drinking with no more ado.
I fetch them bread, fruit, cheese and water, too;
I say all's right as long as I'm well paid;
'Look in again when your flesh troubles you,
Inside this brothel where we drive our trade'.

But soon the devil's among us flesh and fell,
When penniless to bed comes Madge my whore;
I loathe the very sight of her like hell.
I snatch gown, girdle, surcoat, all she wore,
And tell her, these shall stand against her score.
She grips her hips with both hands, cursing God,
Swearing by Jesus' body, bones and blood,
That they shall not. Then I, no whit dismayed
Cross her cracked nose with some stray shiver of wood
Inside this brothel where we drive our trade.

When all's up she drops me a windy word,
Bloat like a beetle puffed and poisonous:
Grins, thumps my pate, and calls me dickey-bird,
And cuffs me with a fist that's ponderous.
We sleep like logs, being drunken both of us;

Then when we wake her womb begins to stir;
To save her seed she gets me under her
Wheezing and whining, flat as planks are laid:
And thus she spoils me for a whoremonger
Inside this brothel where we drive our trade.

Blow, hail or freeze, I've bread here baked rent free!
Whoring's my trade, and my whore pleases me;
Bad cat, bad rat; we're just the same if weighed,
We that love filth, filth follows us, you see;
Honour flies from us, from her we flee
Inside this brothel where we drive our trade.

FRANÇOIS VILLON

The Pig

It was an evening in November,
As I very well remember,
I was strolling down the street in drunken pride,
But my knees were all a-flutter,
And I landed in the gutter
And a pig came up and lay down by my side.

Yes, I lay there in the gutter
Thinking thoughts I could not utter,
When a colleen passing by did softly say
"Ye can tell a man that boozes
By the company he chooses."
And the pig got up and slowly walked away.

ANON

71

Low Down Dirty Shame Blues

I looked out my window, saw a poor boy walkin' in the rain
Yeah looked out my window, saw a poor boy walkin' in the rain
Heard him mutter, "It's a low down dirty shame.

"I walked the streets all night long, got my feet all soakin' wet
Walked the streets all night long, feet all soakin' wet
Ain't seen nobody look like my baby yet.
It's a low down dirty shame."

JOE TURNER

London

I wander thro' each dirty street,
Near where the dirty Thames does flow,
And mark in every face I meet
Marks of weakness, marks of woe.

In every cry of every Man,
In every Infant's cry of fear,
In every voice in every ban,
The mind-forg'd manacles I hear.

How the chimney-sweeper's cry
Every black'ning church appals;
And the hapless soldier's sigh
Runs in blood down palace walls.

But most thro' midnight streets I hear
How the youthful harlot's curse

Blasts the new-born infant's tear,
And blights with plagues the marriage hearse.

WILLIAM BLAKE

Faded Glamour

This used to be the grandest part of town –
now it's all scuffed up, and subsiding into the ground.
There's been markets, garbage riots, Maydays and meteors in the streets –
today, it's just a place where we meet –
and I tell you about sleeping lions, slates and pool-halls –
and you tell me about cheap tequila, place-names and fruit machines,
and I know you're always lying,
but it gets me every time.

Down there's the place we dressed up as mermaids for the day –
all tinsel, nylon and brocade,
and your sunglasses stuck with sequins from the shop down at the end,
that sells unlabelled tin cans – you just guess what you're going to get –
and I tell you this faded glamour's a stupid art-school idea,
and you tell me I don't know either, because I don't have to live here.
I could move away – probably will some day.
But you know what this faded glamour does to me –
don't you know what your faded glamour does to me –
it gets me every time.

We could just walk around
we could just walk all over town
when there's nothing left to say.

HUGH BARKER

The Higher Pantheism in a Nutshell

One, who is not, we see; but one, whom we see not, is;
Surely, this is not that; but that is assuredly this.

What, and wherefore, and whence: for under is over
        and under;
If thunder could be without lightning, lightning could
        be without thunder.

Doubt is faith in the main; but faith, on the whole,
        is doubt;
We cannot believe by proof; but could we believe without?

Why, and whither, and how; for barley and rye are
        not clover;
Neither are straight lines curves; yet over is under
        and over.

One and two are not one; but one and nothing is two;
Truth can hardly be false if falsehood cannot be true.

Parallels all things are; yet many of these are askew;
You are certainly I; but certainly I am not you.

One, who we see not, is; and one, who is not, we see;
Fiddle, we know, is diddle; and diddle, we take it, is dee.

ALGERNON SWINBURNE

Do the Dead Know What Time It Is?

The old guy put down his beer.
Son, he said,
          (and a girl came over to the table where we were:
          asked us by Jack Christ to buy her a drink.)
Son, I am going to tell you something
The like of which nobody ever was told.
          (and the girl said, I've got nothing on tonight;
          how about you and me going to your place?)
I am going to tell you the story of my mother's
Meeting with God.
          (and I whispered to the girl: I don't have a room,
          but, maybe . . .)
She walked up to where the top of the world is
And He came right up to her and said
So at last you've come home.
          (but maybe what?
          I thought I'd like to stay here and talk to you.)
My mother started to cry and God
Put His arms around her.
          (about what?
          Oh, just talk . . . we'll find something.)
She said it was like a fog coming over her face
And light was everywhere and a soft voice saying
You can stop crying now.
          (what can we talk about that will take all night?
          and I said that I didn't know.)
You can stop crying now.

KENNETH PATCHEN

75

One Bad Word

FOR MY BLACK AND ASIAN FRIENDS WHO ARE SHOUTED AT IN THE STREETS

You call me that bad word
That one bad word
That bad word weighs a thousand tonne
That one bad word burns my skin all over
You call me one bad word
That word makes my mother
Cast down her eyes in shame
Makes my father
Deny his own name
Makes my brother
Turn and fight like a demon
Makes my sister
Spend her life in bad dreaming
So call me one bad word
And you don't know what will happen
It could be tears it could be blood
It could be storm
It could be silence
It could be a rage
Hot enough to burn the whole town down
Could be a stampede of elephants
Through your back garden
And into your mother's
Frilly perfume sitting room.
Could be zombie nightmares
Every night for the rest
Of your natural life
Could be all your food

From this day on
Will taste of rotten fishheads
Could be anything
Could be the end of the world
But most likely
This will follow:

I'll stare at you
For one cold second
And then I'll turn and walk away from you
Leaving you alone with yourself
And your one bad word

ADRIAN MITCHELL

Third Time Unlucky

ghosts playing dice
with dice made of ice
they let you win once
they let you win twice

ADRIAN MITCHELL

At the Railway Station, Upway

"There is not much that I can do,
    For I've no money that's quite my own!"
    Spoke up the pitying child –
A little boy with a violin
At the station before the train came in,
"But I can play my fiddle to you,
And a nice one 'tis, and good in tone!"

    The man in the handcuffs smiled;
The constable looked, and he smiled, too,
    As the fiddle began to twang;
And the man in the handcuffs suddenly sang
        With grimful glee:
        "This life so free
        Is the thing for me!"
And the constable smiled, and said no word,
As if unconscious of what he heard;
And so they went on till the train came in –
The convict, and boy with the violin.

THOMAS HARDY

Foreign

Imagine living in a strange, dark city for twenty years.
There are some dismal dwellings on the east side
and one of them is yours. On the landing, you hear
your foreign accent echo down the stairs. You think
in a language of your own and talk in theirs.

Then you are writing home. The voice in your head
recites the letter in a local dialect; behind that
is the sound of your mother singing to you,
all that time ago, and now you do not know
why your eyes are watering and what's the word for this.

You use the public transport. Work. Sleep. Imagine one night
you saw a name for yourself sprayed in red
against a brick wall. A hate name. Red like blood.
It is snowing on the streets, under the neon lights,
as if this place were coming to bits before your eyes.

And in the delicatessen, from time to time, the coins
in your palm will not translate. Inarticulate,
because this is not home, you point at fruit. Imagine
that one of you says *Me not know what these people mean.
It like they only go to bed and dream.* Imagine that.

CAROL ANN DUFFY

Birmingham

Got a wife, got a family
Earn my livin' with my hand
I'm a roller in a steel mill
In downtown Birmingham

My daddy was a barber
And a most unsightly man
He was born in Tuscaloosa
But he died right here in Birmingham

Birmingham, Birmingham
The greatest city in Alabam'
You can travel 'cross this entire land
But there ain't no place like Birmingham

Got a wife named Mary
But she's called Marie
We live in a three room house
With a pepper tree
and I work all day in the factory
That's alright with me

Got a big black dog
His name is Dan
Who lives in my backyard in Birmingham
He is the meanest dog in Alabam'
Get 'em Dan

Birmingham, Birmingham
The greatest city in Alabam'
You can travel 'cross this entire land
But there ain't no place like Birmingham

RANDY NEWMAN

Muliebrity

I have thought so much about the girl
who gathered cow-dung in a wide, round basket
along the main road passing by our house
and the Radhavallabh temple in Maninagar.
I have thought so much about the way she
moved her hands and her waist
and the smell of cow-dung and road-dust and wet canna lilies,
the smell of monkey breath and freshly washed clothes
and the dust from crows' wings which smells different –
and again the smell of cow-dung as the girl scoops
it up, all these smells surrounding me separately
and simultaneously – I have thought so much
but have been unwilling to use her for a metaphor,
for a nice image – but most of all unwilling
to forget her or to explain to anyone the greatness
and the power glistening through her cheekbones
each time she found a particularly promising
mound of dung –

SUJATA BHATT

Ray's Workshop

The air inside is thick.
Sawdust clogs the throat and sticks
in the nostrils, half buries
the sprawled pick-a-stick planks,
settles in drifts over solid
grey and green, steel machinery.

Windows guard against the light
curtained by a clutter
of wooden frames. Cobwebs
stretched over canyons, form
flimsy networks, connecting
nothing to nowhere.

A motorway jam of bottles, pots and jars
jostle on shelves. Flexes coil and snake
round silvery drills, indestructible.
Blue plastic rope splashes colour.
Chisels cluster on workbenches.
Chairs are chained to the ceiling.

In this workshop's disorderly kitchen
sandpaper lines the cake tins
and saucepans are sticky with glue soup.
Cement sets to rock in icecream trays
brushes spill from biscuit boxes
and pins and screws pack coffee tins.

Coated abrasives, nibblers, de-icers
steel wool, enamel thinners, hardened
paints, spark plugs and tube benders
a farmer's mask, record multi-plane
stripper, sealant, and stikit disks
lie dusty together.

Alone in this workshop the man constructs
a framework for his house: doors
and casements, beams and bedsteads
built from ancient reclaimed oak;
a storm casualty becomes
a glowing cedarwood floor.

His carvings in fruitwood and lime,
of lattice-work, ferns and flowers, form
a bolt-hole from the muddle. He can forget
the makeshift ladder in the orchard
propped against a leafless apple tree
that marks the wintertime.

CICELY HERBERT

How to Make a Chandelier

I can't wake up
The sky's too dull to rouse me
Slap my face, try to see my body walk
as other people see me –
but who knows?

It's all out there –
wet boxes, men polishing red cars
Why?
Tin cans and a rain of broken glass
from a smashed car window there

It was me who broke it anyway –
the other night when I was braver
All the pieces of glass
look like diamonds or crystals

I try to pick them up
I try to scoop them all up
Thought I could make a chandelier
but I only cut my hand

So I sneak away
and go to the shop
ten oranges a pound, please –
put them in the fridge for later

HANK STARRS

East St O'Neal

Someone got shot dead round here –
People left flowers by the ribena stains
on the pavement –
Friends, neighbours, strangers –
a million blooms, one day dusty,
the next wet and ragged. So guess what?
I took them all home with me
in a wheelbarrow, filled the bathroom
from floor to ceiling – and listen –
there was no divine damnation,
no cosmic retribution. Once the petals wilted,
I pressed them all flat
in the largest book I've got.
On wet days, the ghost sits
in the kitchen, leafing through it.
He's not grey nor wraith-like,
but bright and solid, like a new bike.
He looks at the faded colours
and plays the radio too loud
and makes a damn mess
of fag-butts and tea leaves.

HANK STARRS

from Jambo

Jambo lives in a street called "No Ball Games". It must be – there's no other street signs left on the estate. The council never bother about putting the names back up. All the fire-engines and taxis and ambulances get lost every time they come here.

The council can't afford to build playgrounds. And they can't afford to replace street names. But they can always manage to come round and put up brand new signs saying "No Ball Games". Then the kids just rip them down again. It's the only game left to play.

Jambo doesn't like watching telly. But the telly likes watching him. It would watch him all day if he'd let it. Right through the kids' stuff in the morning, right through the racing in the afternoon, right through the news, and the film, and the news, and the film and the snooker. Right till it's time to turn off. The telly likes to watch Jambo.

Just to see what he does all day. Picking his nose, picking his feet, picking out winners, falling asleep. Getting up to make a cup of tea, then letting it go cold beside him on the floor. Scratching himself and reading the paper. Wondering whether to go out. Wondering if his mates are coming round. Looking at the time. Picking his nose. Falling asleep.

The telly likes to watch Jambo. Right till it's time to turn off. Just to make sure he wakes up in time to go to bed.

Jambo would like to be a rock star. But he can't play the guitar.
He's tried often enough but he can never quite get the hang of it.

He's going great for a week or two. Deposit down on a brand new
guitar, doing all the chords and fingering. But then just when
he's really getting into it, the shop comes and takes the guitar
back off him because he's forgotten to keep up the payments.

Jambo wants to be the first rock 'n' roll star to go on tour when
he's dead.

He hasn't quite sorted the stage act out, but he knows it'll be a
sensation. Everyone'll be there to see it.

And the live album of the tour's bound to sell millions as well.
Rock 'n' roll stars always make more money when they're dead.

If anything bends, Jambo will bend it.

If anything breaks, Jambo will break it.

If anything is set solid in concrete, Jambo will have to lean on it,
just to see if it moves.

He knows that if he doesn't, Jambo will end up being the one who
gets leaned on, bent and broken.

DAVE WARD

Stagger Lee

The night was clear and the moon was yellow;
And the leaves came tumbling down…

I was standing on the corner
When I heard my bulldog bark,
He was barking at the two men
Who were gambling in the dark.

It was Stagger Lee and Billy,
Two men who gamble late,
Stagger Lee threw seven,
Billy swore that he threw eight.
Look out now – Go, go, Stagger Lee . . .

Stagger Lee told Billy,
"I can't let you go with that,
You have won all my money
And my brand new Stetson hat."

Stagger Lee went home
And he got his forty-four.
Said, "I'm going to the bar room
Just to pay that debt I owe."
Look out now – Go, go Stagger Lee . . .

Stagger Lee went to the bar room
And he stood across the bar room door,
Said, "Now nobody move,"
And he pulled his forty-four.

"Stagger Lee," cried Billy,
"Oh, please don't take my life,
I got three little children
And a very sickly wife."

Stagger Lee shot Billy
Oh, he shot that poor boy so bad
Till the bullet came through Billy
And it broke the bartender's glass –
Look out now – Go, go, Stagger Lee . . .

HAROLD LOGAN and LLOYD PRICE

Sparkles From the Wheel

Where the city's ceaseless crowd moves on the livelong
        day,
Withdrawn I join a group of children watching, I pause
        aside with them.

By the curb toward the edge of the flagging,
A knife-grinder works at his wheel sharpening a great
        knife,
Bending over he carefully holds it to the stone, by foot
        and knee,
With measured tread he turns rapidly, as he presses
        with light but firm hand,
Forth issue then in copious golden jets,
Sparkles from the wheel.

WALT WHITMAN

Near the Moon

If the sun were the dome of St Paul's,
Mars rode round the Circle Line,
Neptune the M25,
and Earth strolled down Church Street,
looking for second hand clothes –
we'd be out in space somewhere
near the moon, just looking down
at all this debris.

We got these chairs from a skip
so we could sit out on the roof
and observe the chaos below –
and watch the lights start flickering on
in ugly concrete blocks against the sky.

Isn't it fine, this time of night –
well you know how
we're always nearly but not quite
where we want to be.
Well I'm nearer now.

We'd be out in space
somewhere near the moon
just looking down in awe.

Can you see us now
somewhere out
near the moon.

HUGH BARKER

Riot in Cell Block Number Nine

On July the second, nineteen-fifty-three
I was servin' time for armed robbery
At four in the mornin' I was sleepin' in my cell
I heard a whistle blow then I heard somebody yell
> There's a riot goin' on
> There's a riot goin' on
There's a riot goin' on up in cell block number nine

The trouble started in cell block number four
It spread like fire across the prison floor
I said, "OK boys get ready to run
Here come the warden, with a tommy gun"
> There's a riot goin' on
> There's a riot goin' on
There's a riot goin' on up in cell block number nine

The warden said, "Come out with your hands up in the air
If you don't stop this riot, you're all gonna get the chair."
Scarface Jones said, "It's too late to quit
Pass the dynamite, cause the . . . fuse is lit"
> There's a riot goin' on
> There's a riot goin' on
There's a riot goin' on up in cell block number nine

In the forty-seventh hour, the tear gas got our men
We're all back in our cells, but every now and then,
> There's a riot goin' on
> There's a riot goin' on
There's a riot goin' on up in cell block number nine

JERRY LEIBER and MIKE STOLLER

Subterranean Homesick Blues

Johnny's in the basement
Mixing up the medicine
I'm on the pavement
Thinking about the government
The man in the trench coat
Badge out, laid off
Says he's got a bad cough
Wants to get it paid off
Look out kid
It's somethin' you did
God knows when
But you're doin' it again
You better duck down the alley way
Lookin' for a new friend
The man in the coon-skin cap
In the big pen
Wants eleven dollar bills
You only got ten

Maggie comes fleet foot
Face full of black soot
Talkin' that the heat put
Plants in the bed but
The phone's tapped anyway
Maggie says that many say
They must bust in early May
Orders from the DA
Look out kid

Don't matter what you did
Walk on your tip toes
Don't try "No Doz"
Better stay away from those
That carry around a fire hose
Keep a clean nose
Watch the plain clothes
You don't need a weather man
To know which way the wind blows

Get sick, get well
Hang around a ink well
Ring bell, hard to tell
If anything is goin' to sell
Try hard, get barred
Get back, write braille
Get jailed, jump bail
Join the army, if you fail
Look out kid
You're gonna get hit
But users, cheaters
Six-time losers
Hang around the theaters
Girl by the whirlpool
Lookin' for a new fool
Don't follow leaders
Watch the parkin' meters

Ah get born, keep warm
Short pants, romance, learn to dance
Get dressed, get blessed
Try to be a success
Please her, please him, buy gifts
Don't steal, don't lift
Twenty years of schoolin'
And they put you on the day shift
Look out kid
They keep it all hid
Better jump down a manhole
Light yourself a candle
Don't wear sandals
Try to avoid the scandals
Don't wanna be a bum
You better chew gum
The pump don't work
'Cause the vandals took the handles

BOB DYLAN

RIVER DEEP MOUNTAIN HIGH

locked safely in the Victorian Bathroom
watching the old iron tub fill up
with boiling rusty water –
both of you daydreaming of
a cool green holiday in the country

Romance

I will make you brooches and toys for your delight
Of bird-song at morning and star-shine at night.
I will make a palace fit for you and me,
Of green days in forests and blue days at sea.

I will make my kitchen, and you shall keep your room,
Where white flows the river and bright blows the broom,
And you shall wash your linen and keep your body white
In rainfall at morning and dewfall at night.

And this shall be for music when no one else is near,
The fine song for singing, the rare song to hear!
That only I remember, that only you admire,
Of the broad road that stretches and the roadside fire.

ROBERT LOUIS STEVENSON

Tall Nettles

Tall nettles cover up, as they have done
These many springs, the rusty harrow, the plough
Long worn out, and the roller made of stone:
Only the elm butt tops the nettles now.

This corner of the farmyard I like most:
As well as any bloom upon a flower
I like the dust on the nettles, never lost
Except to prove the sweetness of a shower.

EDWARD THOMAS

The Mirror in the Woods

A mirror hung on the broken
Walls of an old summer house
Deep in the dark woods. Nothing
Ever moved in it but the
Undersea shadows of ferns,
Rhododendrons and redwoods.
Moss covered the frame. One day
The gold and glue gave way and
The mirror slipped to the floor.
For many more years it stood
On the shattered boards. Once in
A long time a wood rat would
Pass it by without ever
Looking in. At last we came,
Breaking the sagging door and
Letting in a narrow wedge
Of sunlight. We took the mirror
Away and hung it in my
Daughter's room with a barre before
It. Now it reflects ronds, escartes,
Relevés and arabesques.
In the old house the shadows,
The wood rats and moss work unseen.

KENNETH REXROTH

Moggy at Grimma's

Fee-fi-fo-fum and look at the plunge in Grimma's Arden!
Watch the slips, they're a bit properly. Cold my grand.
The gog won't hurt you, he's a blood moggy.
Flat him! Bently! He won't fight, he's only breaking.
A gnashy noise. Brown, Pincer, Brown!
The brass is blush and clamp. The bones are green.

See the clash? Under the breeds?
Goldsplishes and polyglots. Frigs.
All lippery. Mutes under the leavings.
It's all crud at the bottom.
Woeful! Be woeful, brawling, don't want to brumble,
you'll get all brat.

Grimma's mouse smells molish and purey.
The more's lippery. What's in the hubbub? Names!
Sacks of pards, bluedo and pelicans –
when you are older Grimma will play with you,
snappy fumblies, widdley tinks, necks and sadders.
You can go worst because you are longest.

The cock kicks. Grimma binds up the cock
with her big clay. She grinds and grinds.
The cock goes knick, knock and the time goes bong.

Meet your tickies up. Link up your silk.
It's in your very grown hug with the habits on.
How many habits? Gone. Who me! Oh suck
at all those hums! Fetch the weaver,
weep up the hums, all heat and sidey.

Up in the pilchard there are asps
at the blindfold mopples, huzzing in the blowers,
wipe moreberries under the knotting. This one's all dead,
bawling. Meet it up! And a mother!

Look how star you can be from here – proud arrows
boating over the sills and alleys, folds and goods,
bright out to the freeside across the way.

Roamtime now. Say butterfly to Grimma, wailing.
Grieve her a miss, grieve her a shrug –
sun again moon! She bends by the floor and braves.
She braves and braves as Moggy thrives away.

DOROTHY NIMMO

A Mill

Two leaps the water from its race
Made to the brook below,
The first leap it was curving glass,
The second bounding snow.

WILLIAM ALLINGHAM

For Forest

Forest could keep secrets
Forest could keep secrets

Forest tune in everyday
to watersound and birdsound
Forest letting her hair down
to the teeming creeping of her forest-ground

But Forest don't broadcast her business
no Forest cover her business down
from sky and fast-eye sun
and when night come
and darkness wrap her like a gown
Forest is a bad dream woman

Forest dreaming about mountain
and when earth was young
Forest dreaming of the caress of gold
Forest rootsing with mysterious eldorado

and when howler monkey
wake her up with howl
Forest just stretch and stir
to a new day of sound

but coming back to secrets
Forest could keep secrets
Forest could keep secrets
            And we must keep Forest

GRACE NICHOLS

Looking Up

The hot air balloon convention floats
above our garden – weeks pass
but no one wants to come down.
At first the firemen stood by, ready
with their longest ladders,
their life nets and jumping sheets.
But now they've taken off
in their own, fire-red, hot air balloons:
Giant fireballs that dare to compete with the sun.
Who can look after the roses when the sky
ripples and throbs with so much passion?
Our neighbour's attic window glitters balloon-mad
and nostalgic for another life.
Yesterday's sunflower stares and stares.
The birch trees twitch restless
and can't get rid of their spores.
Only the children speak gently
as they collect snails
and line them up along the stone wall.

SUJATA BHATT

Blue Toboggans

scarves for the apaches
wet gloves for snowballs
whoops for white clouds
and blue toboggans

stamping for a tingle
lamps for four o'clock
steamed glass for buses
and blue toboggans

tuning-forks for Wenceslas
white fogs for Prestwick
mince pies for the Eventides
and blue toboggans

TV for the lonely
a long haul for heaven
a shilling for the gas
and blue toboggans

EDWIN MORGAN

Day With George

You have had your white hair cut.
Your son resembles you closely.

Memories slip across
The even landscape.
Gauntlets of close packed
Road cones,
Heading for the cool zone.

Hearing less, you still make
Plans to set the fiddle flying.
Voice colliding, notions stride,
And bareback stream
Towards their home.

Let us eat our meal
Near sunlight
With white polystyrene
Apple juice,
Brown slices,
And small packets of
Butter wrapped in gold.

PAUL MCCARTNEY

The Dong With the Luminous Nose

When awful darkness and silence reign
Over the great Gromboolian plain,
     Through the long, long wintry nights; –
When the angry breakers roar
As they beat on the rocky shore; –
     When Storm-clouds brood on the towering heights
Of the Hills of the Chankly Bore: –
Then, through the vast and gloomy dark,
There moves what seems a fiery spark,
     A lonely spark with silvery rays
     Piercing the coal-black night, –
     A Meteor strange and bright: –
Hither and thither the vision strays,
     A single lurid light.

Slowly it wanders, – pauses, – creeps, –
Anon it sparkles, – flashes and leaps;
And ever as onward it gleaming goes
A light on the Bong-tree stems it throws.
And those who watch at that midnight hour
From Hall or Terrace, or lofty Tower,
Cry, as the wild light passes along, –
     "The Dong! – the Dong!
The wandering Dong through the forest goes!
     The Dong! the Dong!
The Dong with a luminous Nose!"

     Long years ago
     The Dong was happy and gay,

Till he fell in love with a Jumbly Girl
      Who came to those shores one day,
For the Jumblies came in a sieve, they did, –
Landing at eve near the Zemmery Fidd
       Where the Oblong Oysters grow,
     And the rocks are smooth and gray.
And all the woods and the valleys rang
With the Chorus they daily and nightly sang, –
      "Far and few, far and few,
      Are the lands where the Jumblies live;
      Their heads are green, and their hands are blue
      And they went to sea in a sieve."

Happily, happily passed those days!
      While the cheerful Jumblies staid;
    They danced in circlets all night long,
    To the plaintive pipe of the lively Dong,
      In moonlight, shine, or shade.
For day and night he was always there
By the side of the Jumbly Girl so fair,
With her sky-blue hands, and her sea-green hair.
Till the morning came of that hateful day
When the Jumblies sailed in their sieve away,
And the Dong was left on the cruel shore
Gazing – gazing for evermore, –
Ever keeping his weary eyes on
That pea-green sail on the far horizon, –
Singing the Jumbly Chorus still
As he sate all day on the grassy hill, –

"Far and few, far and few,
Are the lands where the Jumblies live;
Their heads are green, and their hands are blue
And they went to sea in a sieve."

But when the sun was low in the West,
      The Dong arose and said; –
– "What little sense I once possessed
      Has quite gone out of my head!" –
And since that day he wanders still
By lake and forest, marsh and hill,
Singing – "O somewhere, in valley or plain
Might I find my Jumbly Girl again!
For ever I'll seek by lake and shore
Till I find my Jumbly Girl once more!"

      Playing a pipe with silvery squeaks,
      Since then his Jumbly Girl he seeks,
      And because by night he could not see,
      He gathered the bark of the Twangum Tree
            On the flowery plain that grows.
            And he wove him a wondrous Nose, –
      A Nose as strange as a Nose could be!
Of vast proportions and painted red,
And tied with cords to the back of his head.
      – In a hollow rounded space it ended
      With a luminous Lamp within suspended,
      All fenced about
      With a bandage stout
      To prevent the wind from blowing it out; –

And with holes all round to send the light,
In gleaming rays on the dismal night.

And now each night, and all night long,
Over those plains still roams the Dong;
And above the wail of the Chimp and Snipe
You may hear the squeak of his plaintive pipe
While ever he seeks, but seeks in vain
To meet with his Jumbly Girl again;
Lonely and wild – all night he goes, –
The Dong with a luminous Nose!
And all who watch at the midnight hour,
From Hall or Terrace, or lofty Tower,
Cry, as they trace the Meteor bright,
Moving along through the dreary night, –
          "This is the hour when forth he goes,
          the Dong with a luminous Nose!
          Yonder – over the plain he goes;
                    He goes!
                    He goes;
          The Dong with the luminous Nose!"

EDWARD LEAR

107

Full Moon and Little Frieda

A cool small evening shrunk to a dog bark and the
      clank of a bucket –

And you listening.
A spider's web, tense for the dew's touch.
A pail lifted, still and brimming – mirror
To tempt a first star to a tremor.

Cows are going home in the lane there, looping the
      hedges with their warm wreaths of breath –
A dark river of blood, many boulders,
Balancing unspilled milk.

"Moon!" you cry suddenly, "Moon! Moon!"
The moon has stepped back like an artist gazing
      amazed at a work
That points at him amazed.

TED HUGHES

from Song of Myself

A child said *What is the grass?* fetching it to me with full hands;
How could I answer the child? I do not know what it is any
      more than he.

I guess it must be the flag of my disposition, out of hopeful green
      stuff woven.

Or I guess it is the handkerchief of the Lord,
A scented gift and remembrancer designedly dropt,
Bearing the owner's name someway in the corners, that we may
      see and remark, and say *Whose?*

Or I guess the grass is itself a child, the produced babe of the
      vegetation.

Or I guess it is a uniform hieroglyphic,
And it means, Sprouting alike in broad zones and narrow zones,
Growing among black folks as among white,
Kanuck, Tuckahoe, Congressman, Cuff, I give them the same, I
      receive them the same.

And now it seems to me the beautiful uncut hair of graves.

Tenderly will I use you curling grass,
It may be you transpire from the breasts of young men,
It may be if I had known them I would have loved them,
It may be you are from old people, or from offspring taken soon
      out of their mothers' laps,
And here you are the mothers' laps.

This grass is very dark to be from the white heads of old mothers,
Darker than the colorless beards of old men,
Dark to come from under the faint red roofs of mouths.

O I perceive after all so many uttering tongues,
And I perceive they do not come from the roofs of mouths for
      nothing.

I wish I could translate the hints about the dead young men and
      women.
And the hints about old men and mothers, and the offspring taken
      soon out of their laps.

What do you think has become of the young and old men?
And what do you think has become of the women and children?

They are alive and well somewhere,
The smallest sprout shows there is really no death,
And if ever there was it led forward life, and does not wait at the
      end to arrest it,
And ceas'd the moment life appear'd.

All goes onward and outward, nothing collapses,
And to die is different from what any one supposed, and luckier.

WALT WHITMAN

TEARS OF RAGE

a Triangular Loft in the roof
an attic full of rebels
arguing out their anger
spelling out their grief –
and everyone ends up
bumping their head

What Happens

It has happened
and it goes on happening
and will happen again
if nothing happens to stop it

The innocent know nothing
because they are too innocent
and the guilty know nothing
because they are too guilty

The poor do not notice
because they are too poor
and the rich do not notice
because they are too rich

The stupid shrug their shoulders
because they are too stupid
and the clever shrug their shoulders
because they are too clever

The young do not care
because they are too young
and the old do not care
because they are too old

That is why nothing happens
to stop it
and that is why it has happened
and goes on happening and will happen again

ERICH FRIED

God Bless the Poor?

I keep seeing the phrase
"God bless the poor."
Who first wrote it down –
that ultimate cop-out,
the most perfectly passed buck in history –
passed on and on till it lands
on God's desk
where we need pay it no attention?
"God bless the poor"
It's found everywhere –
scraped on pyramids,
cast in runes, writ in gold script in churches,
on pompous memorials,
on drinking fountains in municipal gardens –
It runs like a pious stream of piss through history –
"God bless the poor"
Did the poor scratch it themselves on pyramids?
Did they crawl through vaulted churches on bleeding knees
in order to write it?
And did Jesus really say it?
Maybe him with pale skin and blue eyes
and the freshly laundered smock
and the nice new sandals,
Maybe that fraud,
But Jesus?
No, it's likely to be a bad translation,
or a cunning adaptation
made by the early owners of language.
Maybe it ought to have been,

"God inspire the poor" or
"God inflame the poor"
But not "God bless the poor", never that!
For the poor are usually passive,
on their knees, heads bowed humbly –
perfectly positioned for the beheading,
and they need to be tossed
far more than the occasional blessing.

BRIAN PATTEN

A Glass of Beer

The lanky hank of a she in the inn over there
Nearly killed me for asking the loan of a glass of beer;
May the devil grip the whey-faced slut by the hair,
And beat bad manners out of her skin for a year.

That parboiled ape, with the toughest jaw you will see
On virtue's path, and a voice that would rasp the dead,
Came roaring and raging the minute she looked at me,
And threw me out of the house on the back of my head!

If I asked her master he'd give me a cask a day;
But she, with the beer at hand, not a gill would arrange!
May she marry a ghost and bear him a kitten, and may
The High King of Glory permit her to get the mange.

JAMES STEPHENS

The Lie

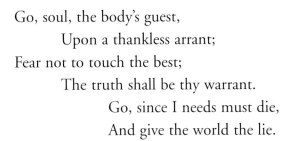

Go, soul, the body's guest,
    Upon a thankless arrant;
Fear not to touch the best;
    The truth shall be thy warrant.
        Go, since I needs must die,
        And give the world the lie.

Say to the court, it glows
    And shines like rotten wood;
Say to the church, it shows
    What's good, and doth no good:
        If church and court reply,
        Then give them both the lie.

Tell potentates, they live
    Acting by others' action,
Not loved unless they give,
    Not strong but by their faction:
        If potentates reply,
        Give potentates the lie.

Tell men of high condition
    That manage the estate,
Their purpose is ambition,
    Their practice only hate:
        And if they once reply,
        Then give them all the lie.

Tell them that brave it most,
  They beg for more by spending,
Who, in their greatest cost,
  Seek nothing but commending:
    And if they make reply,
    Then give them all the lie.

Tell zeal it wants devotion;
  Tell love it is but lust;
Tell time it is but motion;
  Tell flesh it is but dust:
    And wish them not reply,
    For thou must give the lie.

Tell age it daily wasteth;
  Tell honour how it alters;
Tell beauty how she blasteth;
  Tell favour how it falters:
    And as they shall reply,
    Give every one the lie.

Tell wit how much it wrangles
  In tickle points of niceness;
Tell wisdom she entangles
  Herself in over-wiseness:
    And when they do reply,
    Straight give them both the lie.

Tell physic of her boldness;
  Tell skill it is prevention;
Tell charity of coldness;

Tell law it is contention:
    And as they do reply,
    So give them still the lie.

Tell fortune of her blindness;
    Tell nature of decay;
Tell friendship of unkindness;
    Tell justice of delay:
      And if they will reply,
      Then give them all the lie.

Tell arts they have no soundness,
    But vary by esteeming;
Tell schools they want profoundness,
    And stand too much on seeming:
      If arts and schools reply,
      Give arts and schools the lie.

Tell faith it's fled the city;
    Tell how the country erreth;
Tell, manhood shakes off pity;
    Tell, virtue least preferreth:
      And if they do reply,
      Spare not to give the lie.

So when thou hast, as I
    Commanded thee, done blabbing,
Although to give the lie
    Deserves no less than stabbing,
      Stab at thee he that will,
      No stab the soul can kill.

SIR WALTER RALEGH

The Minister for Exams

When I was a child I sat an exam.
The test was so simple
There was no way I could fail.

Q1. Describe the taste of the moon.

It tastes like Creation I wrote,
it has the flavour of starlight.

Q2. What colour is Love?

Love is the colour of water a man
lost in the desert finds, I wrote.

Q3. Why do snowflakes melt?

I wrote, they melt because they fall
onto the warm tongue of God.

There were other questions.
They were as simple.

I described the grief of Adam when he was expelled from Eden.
I wrote down the exact weight of an elephant's dream.

Yet today, many years later,
for my living I sweep the streets
or clean out the toilets of the fat hotels.
Why? Because constantly I failed my exams.

Why? Well, let me set a test.

Q1. How large is a child's imagination?
Q2. How shallow is the soul of the Minister for Exams?

BRIAN PATTEN

Futility

Move him into the sun –
Gently its touch awoke him once,
At home, whispering of fields unsown.
Always it woke him, even in France,
Until this morning and this snow.
If anything might rouse him now
The kind old sun will know.

Think how it wakes the seeds, –
Woke, once, the clays of a cold star.
Are limbs, so dear-achieved, are sides,
Full-nerved – still warm – too hard to stir?
Was it for this the clay grew tall?
– O what made fatuous sunbeams toil
To break earth's sleep at all?

WILFRED OWEN

Villon's Straight Tip to All Cross Coves

"Tout aux tavernes et aux filles"

Suppose you screeve? or go cheap-jack?
          Or fake the broads? or fig a nag?
Or thimble-rig? or knap a yack?
          Or pitch a snide? or smash a rag?
          Suppose you duff? or nose and lag?
Or get the straight, and land your pot?
          How do you melt the multy swag?
Booze and the blowens cop the lot.

Fiddle, or fence, or mace, or mack,
          Or moskeneer, or flash the drag;
Dead-lurk a crib, or do a crack,
          Pad with a slang, or chuck a fag;
          Bonnet, or tout, or mump, and gag;
Rattle the tats, or mark the spot:
          You cannot bag a single stag –
Booze and the blowens cop the lot.

Suppose you try a different tack,
          And on the square you flash your flag?
A penny-a-lining make your whack,
          Or with the mummers mump and gag?
          For nix, for nix the dibs you bag!
At any graft, no matter what,
          Your merry goblins soon stravag –
Booze and the blowens cop the lot.

Envoy
    It's up the spout and Charley Wag
With wipes and tickers and what not;
    Until the squeezer nips your scrag,
Booze and the blowens cop the lot.

FRANÇOIS VILLON

The Chances

I mind as 'ow the night afore that show
Us five got talkin', – we was in the know.
"Over the top to-morrer; boys, we're for it.
First wave we are, first ruddy wave; that's tore it!"
"Ah well," says Jimmy, – an' 'e's seen some scrappin' –
"There ain't no more nor five things as can 'appen:
Ye get knocked out; else wounded – bad or cushy;
Scuppered; or nowt except yer feelin' mushy."

One of us got the knock-out, blown to chops.
T'other was 'urt, like, losin' both 'is props.
An' one, to use the word of 'ypocrites,
'Ad the misfortoon to be took be Fritz.
Now me, I wasn't scratched, praise God Amighty,
(Though next time please I'll thank 'im for a blighty).
But poor young Jim, 'e's livin' an' 'e's not;
'E reckoned 'e'd five chances, an' 'e 'ad;
'E's wounded, killed, and pris'ner, all the lot,
The bloody lot all rolled in one. Jim's mad.

WILFRED OWEN

Many Thousand Gone

No more auction block for me
No more, no more
No more auction block for me
Many thousand gone

No more peck o' corn for me
No more, no more
No more peck o' corn for me
Many thousand gone

No more driver's lash for me
No more, no more
No more driver's lash for me
Many thousand gone

No more pint o' salt for me
No more, no more
No more pint o' salt for me
Many thousand gone

No more hundred lash for me
No more, no more
No more hundred lash for me
Many thousand gone

No more mistress' call for me
No more, no more
No more mistress' call for me
Many thousand gone

ANON

Massacre of the Boys

The children cried "Mummy!
But I have been good!
It's dark in here! Dark!"

See them They are going to the bottom
See the small feet
they went to the bottom Do you see
that print
of a small foot here and there

pockets bulging
with string and stones
and little horses made of wire

A great closed plain
like a figure of geometry
and a tree of black smoke
a vertical
dead tree
with no star in its crown.

TADEUSZ ROZEWICZ

The Visit

A witch showed us a hill of hair,
a hunchback showed us a mountain of pots and pans,
a few still petalled with paint.
Then came a hare
who showed us a hill of shaving-brushes,
a wood of toothbrushes
whose old-fashioned yellow bristles were
worn down to the wood.

What is your fairy story?

Said the old woman.
The bowed old man wasn't her husband,
they had a hare of a grandchild, all ribs
(there is a child, an orphan,
in the triangle of a blanket made of holes
it is dragging as it limps slowly
over and over again).
The short and small and crippled,
the old and the young.

Who planted the handsome poplars?

Temporarily there comes a stone-coloured wall
of rain. Pigs, chickens.
A herd of roistering ponies,
new-fangled houses with balconies,
old-fangled houses.
What is your fairy story?

Absolutely solid and indisputable,
a number of rows of plum-red
brick barracks behind
two rows of electrified barbed wire.

Ever after.

Who planted the poplars,
now queenly, swaying, a kind of veil?

Behind glass
a mountain of dead women's hair.

Rain.

Rain.

JUDITH KAZANTZIS

Collateral Damage

The minor diplomat who brings terms for a ceasefire
Enters through a side-door, in the small hours,
Wearing a belted raincoat.

The children have become bold. At the first siren
They cried, and ran for their mothers.
Now they are worldly-wise,

They clamour to watch dogfights above the house,
They prefer under-the-kitchen-table to the shelter,
They play fighting games

Of reading the paper by bomblight,
Pretending to be the enemy. These children
Are no longer safe.

They have learned rash and contrary for ever. Come soon,
O minor diplomat in the belted raincoat, come
To capitulate. For the children have ack-ack nerves,
And a landmine has fallen next door.

Under the reservoir, under the wind-figured water,
Are the walls, the church, the houses,
The small human things,

That in drought rise up gaunt and dripping,
And it was once Mardale, both is and is not Mardale,
But is still there,

Like the diplomat, and the crazy fearless children
Who progress through their proper stages, and the churchbells
With their nightly riddles,

And the diplomat, and the children still running
Away from shelter, into the path of the bomb.

U. A. FANTHORPE

Advert

Excuse me,
I've got my foot in your front door,
I'll tell you what's what and I'll give you what for,
And I'll wipe the floor and I'll raise the roof,
And I'll burgle your brains with the Gospel Truth.

So hold the front page this is front-page news,
I've got more hubris than Howard Hughes,
I'm going to orate and I know you'll let me,
'Cos you don't deserve me but you're going to get me,
I'll lay down the law and you have no choice,
'Cos I love the sound of my own voice,
I'm Social,
Mr Social Control.

Well now,
You're conformist and I'm so normative
That the only possible critique's performative,
Power's a ghost, now you don't now you see it,
My approach is to actually be it,
I'm like a disease, you can't feel the onset,
But you can't catch me, I'm an abstract concept.
You can't rebel or criticise me,
I'm Social Control, you internalise me.

So I'm standing ranting, up on my plinth,
Waiting for my rider (it's a crate of absinthe),
Can't you feel the power, can't you feel the tension,
Am I rhyming too fast for your comprehension?

Can't you smell the tension, can't you taste the fear?
Well then don't try make me pay for the beer,
'Cos I'm top of the bill and that's a fact,
'Cos no sucker poet wants to follow my act.

And I will rant if you will listen,
And command if you'll obey,
I'll enact if you'll spectate,
And I will market if you'll pay,
If you'll chortle I will quip,
I'll televise if you'll receive,
I'll control if you'll submit,
Hypothesise if you will but believe in me,

So: clear the stage, clear the front page,
Mister Social's in a righteous rage,
Cut up the flag and sample the anthem,
Here come shock slogans and a token tantrum,
You're now entering the social zone,
These facts are ear-shaped ram them home,
I'm coming at yer, coming at yer,
Coming at you like a Velociraptor.

Under my regime you'll be getting it bad,
When London's renamed Socialgrad,
You'll think it's cool but it's a con,
So Stop the State 'cos I want to get on,
Those "New Age" neddies, they'll soon be in shock,
'Cos I got more hoodoo than Papa Doc,
Lickspittle Lefties, they'll come later,
Get down bigboy, flog my paper,

Social work liberals in my care
Are pinned down with a dysfunctional stare,
And for vague-out Greens I'm the best corrective,
They say *Earth First*! I say: get some perspective,
Whatever you say I disagree,
'Cos everyone's wrong except for me.

My head's my stash and my tongue's my GATT,
And my words are bullets so you'd better get flat,
Your slack-jawed vacancy makes me vehement,
Like the Basra Road you're a Target-Rich Environment,
My poems are autonomists cutting down pylons,
You won't catch me rhyming "violence" with "silence",
These platitude-poets don't aid my survival,
They've got nothing to say they're just adjectival.

I'm ecofriendly, I'm superstrength,
I'm family-size and I'm luxury length,
I've got wheelchair access and an all-night crèche,
I'm New Improved and I'm Lemon Fresh,
If poetry's pop, I'm Coca-Cola,
If language is a virus, then I'm giving you Ebola,
I've got words that bite, I've got words that spank,
And I make more marks than the Bundesbank,

When compared to my eloquence,
The very truth's a liar,
For I am Mr Social Control,
The thief of fire.

MR SOCIAL CONTROL

History Never Happened

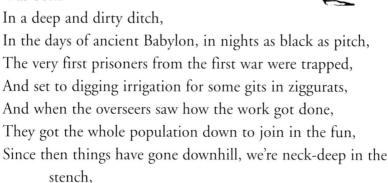

Work
Was born
In a deep and dirty ditch,
In the days of ancient Babylon, in nights as black as pitch,
The very first prisoners from the first war were trapped,
And set to digging irrigation for some gits in ziggurats,
And when the overseers saw how the work got done,
They got the whole population down to join in the fun,
Since then things have gone downhill, we're neck-deep in the
       stench,
History never happened, we're still digging the same trench,
This organised misanthropy puts hatred in my heart,
So I get revenged upon the world by simply taking part,
History, it never happened.

And in the crooked march of centuries the 20th's a blip,
A century of dreams from welfare state to rocketship,
Nye Bevan and Apollo in irrelevant modernity
Fell away to leave us face to face with all eternity,
So the next one is the last one, the pseudo-Victorian fallacy
Began as fancy lamp-posts, ended up as public policy,
So beggars on Gin Alley are cluttering the kerbs,
The Navy is delivering ultimata to the Serbs,
There was no Great Leap Forward and no Treaty of Wien,
You make me feel like it's almost 1815 again.

One time we said we will be poor no more John Maynard Keynes,
And he said, cool, I'll pay you well to make washing machines,
And parts of carburettors and a splendid safety net,

130

To spend your brand-new wages on and make you all forget
That one time you had threatened us, the terms of this petition
Were historically specific as there's no human condition,
Too flexible, too durable, so day by day we manage,
Committing grace and patience and the odd criminal damage.

And when we get on to the salaries of those chaps who run
      British Gas,
We get this rhetorical pronoun, makes us sound like we think
      we're a class,
And when I signed on they were tricking me, into feeling like I
      was thieving,
And I really am totally pig-sick of ducking and diving and
      dodging and weaving,
Holocaust? Which Holocaust? I made it all up in my bedroom,
History's just a mass break-out of the famous False Memory
      Syndrome.

And even then back in Babylon, museums housed the past,
They thought they were the crown of ages come to fruit at last,
A history of gangstas since, writ just to misinform,
Writing itself was devised by bureaucrats using cuneiform,
To proclaim the End of History, stagflation, boom and bust,
All built on the illusion that it ever will be thus,
Which it will if it's allowed to, for there's just one chance I
      get,
That history never happened, as it hasn't started yet.

We enter by the tavern door, we laugh and buy our round,

And really it don't matter, soon enough we're in the ground,
And everything we do, say, love, smell, overthrow or taste,
Was just one single moment in annihilation's waste,
And when the last ten bricks of London are consumed into the
      clay,
When the last of tombs has perished and there's two nights every
      day,
When the Sun's gone supergiant there will be no breath to say,
That history never happened because we let it slip away.

The evolution of chaotic systems
Is characterised by sudden cataclysms,
Highly determined, unexpected transitions,
From one semi-stable state to the next,
The flap of that proverbial butterfly's wing
Looses the lightning above Beijing,
You change the world when you change one thing,
Like in that film.

And we're ready for the kick-off,
Like the First World War,
We're ready for the kick-off,
And all we need's a bullet through a fat arch-duke.

MR SOCIAL CONTROL

Strange Meeting

It seemed that out of battle I escaped
Down some profound dull tunnel, long since scooped
Through granites which titanic wars had groined.
Yet also there encumbered sleepers groaned,
Too fast in thought or death to be bestirred.
Then, as I probed them, one sprang up, and stared
With piteous recognition in fixed eyes,
Lifting distressful hands as if to bless.
And by his smile, I knew that sullen hall,
By his dead smile I knew we stood in Hell.
With a thousand pains that vision's face was grained;
Yet no blood reached there from the upper ground,
And no guns thumped, or down the flues made moan.
"Strange friend," I said, "here is no cause to mourn."
"None," said that other, "save the undone years,
The hopelessness. Whatever hope is yours,
Was my life also; I went hunting wild
After the wildest beauty in the world,
Which lies not calm in eyes, or braided hair,
But mocks the steady running of the hour,
And if it grieves, grieves richlier than here.
For of my glee might many men have laughed.
And of my weeping something had been left,
Which must die now. I mean the truth untold,
The pity of war, the pity war distilled.
Now men will go content with what we spoiled,
Or, discontent, boil bloody, and be spilled.
They will be swift with swiftness of the tigress.
None will break ranks, though nations trek from progress.

Courage was mine, and I had mystery,
Wisdom was mine, and I had mastery:
To miss the march of this retreating world
Into vain citadels that are not walled.
Then, when much blood had clogged their chariot-wheels,
I would go up and wash them from sweet wells,
Even with truths that lie too deep for taint.
I would have poured my spirit without stint
But not through wounds; not on the cess of war.
Foreheads of men have bled where no wounds were.
I am the enemy you killed, my friend.
I knew you in this dark: for so you frowned
Yesterday through me as you jabbed and killed.
I parried; but my hands were loath and cold.
Let us sleep now…"

WILFRED OWEN

Let The Slave *and*
What is the Price of Experience?

Let the slave grinding at the mill run out into the field,
Let him look up into the heavens & laugh in the bright air;
Let the inchained soul, shut up in darkness and in sighing,
Whose face has never seen a smile in thirty weary years,
Rise and look out; his chains are loose, his dungeon doors are open;
And let his wife and children return from the oppressor's scourge.
They look behind at every step & believe it is a dream,
Singing:

The Sun has left his blackness, & has found a fresher morning,
And the fair Moon rejoices in the clear & cloudless night;
For Empire is no more, and now the Lion & Wolf shall cease.

For every thing that lives is Holy
For every thing that lives is Holy . . .

What is the price of Experience? Do men buy it for a song?
Or wisdom for a dance in the street? No, it is bought with the
      price
Of all that a man hath, his house, his wife, his children.
Wisdom is sold in the desolate market where none come to buy
And in the wither'd field where the farmer plows for bread in
      vain.

It is an easy thing to triumph in the summer's sun
And in the vintage, & to sing on the waggon loaded with corn.
It is an easy thing to talk of patience to the afflicted,
To speak the laws of prudence to the houseless wanderer,
To listen to the hungry raven's cry in wintry season
When the red blood is fill'd with wine & with the marrow of
      lambs.

It is an easy thing to laugh at wrathful elements,
To hear the dog howl at the wintry door, the ox in the slaughter
      house moan;
To see a god on every wind & a blessing on every blast;
To hear sounds of love in the thunder storm that destroys our
      enemies' house;
To rejoice in the blight that covers his field, & the sickness that
      cuts off his children,

While our olive and vine sing and laugh round our door,
    & our children bring fruit & flowers.

Then the groan and the dolor are quite forgotten,
    & the slave grinding at the mill,
And the captive in chains, & the poor in the prison,
    & the soldier in the field
When the shatter'd bone hath laid him groaning
    among the happier dead.
It is an easy thing to rejoice in the tents of prosperity:
Thus would I sing & thus rejoice: but it is not so with me.

For every thing that lives is Holy.
For every thing that lives is Holy.
For every thing that lives is Holy.
For every thing that lives is Holy.

WILLIAM BLAKE

The Lament of the Warrior's Wife

The water, clear as a spring, flows on under the bridge.
Nearby, the road is covered with young grass.
I follow you with a heavy heart,
O my husband, my love . . .
I wish I were the horse you ride, the boat you steer,
The river flows on,
But its waters will not wash my tears away;
The young grass smells sweet,
But its perfumes will not soothe my sorrows.

To the resounding beat of the drums,
Despair, mounting like the tide, captures my heart.
Goodbye, goodbye, O my husband, O my love.
My lips whisper goodbye, but my hand remains in your hand.
I go with you but my feet are rooted here.
I wish I were the evening breeze singing in the branches,
To follow you, to sweeten your sleep.

But nothing will hold you here, O my husband, O my love,
Neither family, nor wife, nor child.
Like the Spirit of Hatred, your eyes on fire,
You hurl yourself in the path of the enemy.
You frighten me, O my husband.
The wind trembles as you pass.

Your tunic is red as the rising sun,
Your horse is as white as snow.
With my eyes closed
I heard your horse galloping away over my heart,
His hoofs echoing, echoing, and dying away
Among the rolling drums.

Warriors! From T-Lieu to Trang Duong
There are nothing but warriors,
And leaving with them
Are the sounds of flutes and the colours of flags.
You ride away through the rain and the wind,
O my husband, my love.

I stay alone in our house,
In the same room,
With the same rush mat,
The same coverlet.
The blue clouds burst into tears,
The withered leaves stifle their sobs.
The plain lies all alone.
The mountains are as silent as stone.

O sun, O moon, where is my husband, my love?
O moon, I am afraid of you!
O clouds, I am afraid of you!
I am afraid of the long road and the deep river.
I am afraid of the morning sun
And of the flames dying with the day.
Flow, flow tears, flow down my face, fall on my robe.
Cry, cry, O my eyes!
Cry through the long night of waiting.
O my husband, my love,
I believed I was part of you
As a fish is part of the ocean.
Alas, I have been taken away from you
As water is taken from the clouds.

ANON (VIETNAMESE CLASSICAL POEM)

SISTERS

At least two of the guests
at the party were ghosts –
two young women, one rich, one poor,
holding hands and drifting
through the dancers…

Concerning the Infanticide, Marie Farrar

Marie Farrar, born in April,
No marks, a minor, rachitic, both parents dead,
Allegedly, up to now without police record,
Committed infanticide, it is said,
As follows: in her second month, she says,
With the aid of a barmaid she did her best
To get rid of her child with two douches,
Allegedly painful but without success.
But you, I beg you, check your wrath and scorn
For man needs help from every creature born.

She then paid out, she says, what was agreed
And continued to lace herself up tight.
She also drank liquor with pepper mixed in it
Which purged her but did not cure her plight.
Her body distressed her as she washed the dishes,
It was swollen now quite visibly.
She herself says, for she was still a child,
She prayed to Mary most earnestly.
But you, I beg you, check your wrath and scorn
For man needs help from every creature born.

Her prayers, it seemed, helped her not at all.
She longed for help. Her trouble made her falter
And faint at early mass. Often drops of sweat
Broke out in anguish as she knelt at the altar.
Yet until her time had come upon her
She still kept secret her condition.
For no one believed such a thing had happened,

That she, so unenticing, had yielded to temptation.
But you, I beg you, check your wrath and scorn
For man needs help from every creature born.

And on that day, she says, when it was dawn,
As she washed the stairs it seemed a nail
Was driven into her belly. She was wrung with pain.
But still she secretly endured her travail.
All day long while hanging out the laundry
She racked her brains till she got it through her head
She had to bear the child and her heart was heavy.
It was very late when she went up to bed.
But you, I beg you, check your wrath and scorn
For man needs help from every creature born.

She was sent for again as soon as she lay down:
Snow had fallen and she had to go downstairs.
It went on till eleven. It was a long day.
Only at night did she have time to bear.
And so, she says, she gave birth to a son.
The son she bore was just like all the others.
She was unlike the others but for this
There is no reason to despise this mother.
You too, I beg you, check your wrath and scorn
For man needs help from every creature born.

Accordingly I will go on with the story
Of what happened to the son that came to be.
(She says she will hide nothing that befell)

So let it be a judgement upon both you and me.
She says she had scarcely gone to bed when she
Was overcome with sickness and she was alone,
Not knowing what would happen, yet she still
Contrived to stifle all her moans.
And you, I beg you, check your wrath and scorn
For man needs help from every creature born.

With her last strength, she says, because
Her room had now grown icy cold, she then
Dragged herself to the latrine and there
Gave birth as best she could (not knowing when)
But toward morning. She says she was already
Quite distracted and could barely hold
The child for snow came into the latrine
And her fingers were half numb with cold.
You too, I beg you, check your wrath and scorn
For man needs help from every creature born.

Between the latrine and her room, she says,
Not earlier, the child began to cry until
It drove her mad so that she says
She did not cease to beat it with her fists
Blindly for some time till it was still.
And then she took the body to her bed
And kept it with her there all through the night:
When morning came she hid it in the shed.
But you, I beg you, check your wrath and scorn
For man needs help from every creature born.

Marie Farrar, born in April,
An unmarried mother, convicted, died in
The Meissen penitentiary,
She brings home to you all men's sin.
You who bear pleasantly between clean sheets
And give the name "blessed" to your womb's weight
Must not damn the weakness of the outcast,
For her sin was black but her pain was great.
Therefore, I beg you, check your wrath and scorn
For man needs help from every creature born.

BERTHOLT BRECHT

A Royal Princess

I, a princess, king-descended, decked with jewels, gilded, drest,
Would rather be a peasant with her baby at her breast,
For all I shine so like the sun, and am purple like the west.

Two and two my guards behind, two and two before,
Two and two on either hand, they guard me evermore;
Me, poor dove that must not coo – eagle that must not soar.

All my fountains cast up perfumes, all my gardens grow
Scented woods and foreign spices, with all flowers in blow
That are costly, out of season as the seasons go.

All my walls are lost in mirrors, whereupon I trace
Self to right hand, self to left hand, self in every place,
Self-same solitary figure, self-same seeking face.

Then I have an ivory chair high to sit upon,
Almost like my father's chair, which is an ivory throne;
There I sit uplift and upright, there I sit alone.

Alone by day, alone by night, alone days without end;
My father and my mother give me treasures, search and spend –
O my father! O my mother! have you ne'er a friend?

As I am a lofty princess, so my father is
A lofty king, accomplished in all kingly subtlities,
Holding in his strong right hand world-kingdoms' balances.

He has quarrelled with his neighbours, he has scourged his foes;
Vassal counts and princes follow where his pennon goes,
Long-descended valiant lords whom the vulture knows,

On whose track the vulture swoops, when they ride in state
To break the strength of armies and topple down the great:
Each of these my courteous servant, none of these my mate.

My father counting up his strength sets down with equal pen
So many head of cattle, head of horses, head of men;
These for slaughter, these for labour, with the how and when.

Some to work on roads, canals; some to man his ships;
Some to smart in mines beneath sharp overseers' whips;
Some to trap fur-beasts in lands where utmost winter nips.

Once it came into my heart and whelmed me like a flood,
That these too are men and women, human flesh and blood;
Men with hearts and men with souls, tho' trodden down like mud.

Our feasting was not glad that night, our music was not gay;
On my mother's graceful head I marked a thread of grey,
My father frowning at the fare seemed every dish to weigh.

I sat beside them sole princess in my exalted place,
My ladies and my gentlemen stood by me on the dais:
A mirror showed me I look old and haggard in the face;

It showed me that my ladies all are fair to gaze upon,
Plump, plenteous-haired, to every one love's secret lore is known,
They laugh by day, they sleep by night; ah, me, what is a throne?

The singing men and women sang that night as usual,
The dancers danced in pairs and sets, but music had a fall,
A melancholy windy fall as at a funeral.

Amid the toss of torches to my chamber back we swept;
My ladies loosed my golden chain; meantime I could have wept
To think of some in galling chains whether they waked or slept.

I took my bath of scented milk, delicately waited on,
They burned sweet things for my delight, cedar and cinnamon,
They lit my shaded silver lamp, and left me there alone.

A day went by, a week went by. One day I heard it said:
"Men are clamouring, women children, clamouring to be fed;
Men like famished dogs are howling in the streets for bread."

So two whispered by my door, not thinking I could hear,
Vulgar naked truth, ungarnished for a royal ear;
Fit for cooping in the background, not to stalk so near.

But I strained my utmost sense to catch this truth, and mark:
"There are families out grazing, like cattle in the park."
"A pair of peasants must be saved, even if we build an ark."

A merry jest, a merry laugh: each strolled upon his way:
One was my page, a lad I reared and bore with day by day;
One was my youngest maid, as sweet and white as cream in May.

Other footsteps followed softly with a weightier tramp;
Voices said: "Picked soldiers have been summoned from
      the camp,
To quell these base-born ruffians who make free to howl
      and stamp."

"Howl and stamp?" one answered: "They made free to hurl a stone
At the minister's state coach, well aimed and stoutly thrown."
"There's work then for the soldiers, for this rank crop must
      be mown."

"One I saw, a poor old fool with ashes on his head,
Whimpering because a girl had snatched his crust of bread:
Then he dropped; when some one raised him, it turned out he
      was dead."

"After us the deluge," was retorted with a laugh:
"If bread's the staff of life they must walk without a staff."
"While I've a loaf they're welcome to my blessing and the chaff."

These passed. "The king": stand up. Said my father with a smile:
"Daughter mine, your mother comes to sit with you awhile;
She's sad to-day, and who but you her sadness can beguile?"

He too left me. Shall I touch my harp now while I wait, –
(I hear them doubling guard below before our palace gate) –
Or shall I work the last gold stitch into my veil of state;

Or shall my woman stand and read some impassioned scene, –
There's music of a lulling sort in words that pause between;
Or shall she merely fan me while I wait here for the queen?

Again I caught my father's voice in sharp word of command:
"Charge" a clash of steel: "Charge again, the rebels stand.
Smite and spare not, hand to hand; smite and spare not,
      hand to hand."

There swelled a tumult at the gate, high voices waxing higher;
A flash of red reflected light lit the cathedral spire;
I heard a cry for faggots, then I heard a yell for fire.

"Sit and roast there with your meat, sit and bake there
      with your bread,
You who sat to see us starve," one shrieking woman said:
"Sit on your throne and roast with your crown upon your head."

Nay, this thing I will do, while my mother tarrieth,
I will take my fine spun gold, but not to sew therewith,
I will take my gold and gems, and rainbow fan and wreath:

With a ransom in my lap, a king's ransom in my hand,
I will go down to this people, will stand face to face, will stand
Where they curse king, queen, and princess of this cursed land.

They shall take all to buy them bread, take all I have to give;
I, if I perish, perish; they today shall eat and live;
I, if I perish, perish; that's the goal I half conceive:

Once to speak before the world, rend bare my heart and show
The lesson I have learned, which is death, is life, to know.
I, if I perish, perish; in the name of God I go.

CHRISTINA ROSSETTI

THE FIRST TIME EVER I SAW YOUR FACE

songs and poems secretly

tape-recorded

in the cushion-scattered

Smooching Room

because all we need

after all

is love

O Western Wind

O western wind, when wilt thou blow,
That the small rain down may rain?
Christ that my love were in my arms
And I in my bed again!

ANON

A Ditty

My true-love hath my heart, and I have his,
By just exchange one for another given:
I hold his dear, and mine he cannot miss,
There never was a better bargain driven:
        My true-love hath my heart, and I have his.

His heart in me keeps him and me in one,
My heart in him his thoughts and senses guides:
He loves my heart, for once it was his own,
I cherish his because in me it bides:
        My true-love hath my heart, and I have his.

SIR PHILIP SIDNEY

A Puppy Called Puberty

It was like keeping a puppy in your underpants
A secret puppy you weren't allowed to show to anyone
Not even your best friend or your worst enemy

You wanted to pat him stroke him cuddle him
All the time but you weren't supposed to touch him

He only slept for five minutes at a time
Then he'd suddenly perk up his head
In the middle of school medical inspection
And always on bus rides
So you had to climb down from the upper deck
All bent double to smuggle the puppy off the bus
Without the buxom conductress spotting
Your wicked and ticketless stowaway.

Jumping up, wet-nosed, eagerly wagging –
He only stopped being a nuisance
When you were alone together
Pretending to be doing your homework
But really gazing at each other
Through hot and hazy daydreams

Of those beautiful schoolgirls on the bus
With kittens bouncing in their sweaters.

ADRIAN MITCHELL

Against Coupling

I write in praise of the solitary act:
of not feeling a trespassing tongue
forced into one's mouth, one's breath
smothered, nipples crushed against the
ribcage, and that metallic tingling
in the chin set off by a certain odd nerve:

unpleasure. Just to avoid those eyes would help –
such eyes as a young girl draws life from,
listening to the vegetal
rustle within her, as his gaze
stirs polypal fronds in the obscure
sea-bed of her body, and her own eyes blur.

There is much to be said for abandoning
this no longer novel exercise –
for not "participating in
a total experience" – when
one feels like the lady in Leeds who
has seen *The Sound of Music* eighty-six times;

or more, perhaps, like the school drama mistress
producing *A Midsummer Night's Dream*
for the seventh year running, with
yet another cast from 5B.
Pyramus and Thisbe are dead, but
the hole in the wall can still be troublesome.

I advise you, then, to embrace it without
encumbrance. No need to set the scene,
dress up (or undress), make speeches.
Five minutes of solitude are
enough – in the bath, or to fill
that gap between the Sunday papers and lunch.

FLEUR ADCOCK

The Question Answered

What is it men in women do require?
The lineaments of gratified desire.
What is it women do in men require?
The lineaments of gratified desire.

WILLIAM BLAKE

Sally in Our Alley

Of all the girls that are so smart
    There's none like pretty Sally;
She is the darling of my heart,
    And she lives in our alley.
There is no lady in the land
    Is half so sweet as Sally;
She is the darling of my heart,
    And she lives in our alley.

Her father he makes cabbage-nets
    And through the streets does cry 'em;
Her mother she sells laces long
    To such as please to buy 'em:
But sure such folks could ne'er beget
    So sweet a girl as Sally!
She is the darling of my heart,
    And she lives in our alley.

When she is by, I leave my work,
    I love her so sincerely;
My master comes like any Turk,
    And bangs me most severely –
But let him bang his bellyful,
    I'll bear it all for Sally;
She is the darling of my heart,
    And she lives in our alley.

Of all the days that's in the week
    I dearly love but one day –
And that's the day that comes betwixt

A Saturday and Monday;
For then I'm drest all in my best
        To walk abroad with Sally;
She is the darling of my heart,
        And she lives in our alley.

My master carries me to church,
        And often am I blamed
Because I leave him in the lurch
        As soon as text is named;
I leave the church in sermon-time
        And slink away to Sally;
She is the darling of my heart,
        And she lives in our alley.

When Christmas comes about again
        O then I shall have money;
I'll hoard it up, and box it all,
        I'll give it to my honey;
I would it were ten thousand pound,
        I'd give it all to Sally;
She is the darling of my heart,
        And she lives in our alley.

My master and the neighbours all
        Make game of me and Sally,
And, but for her, I'd better be
        A slave and row a galley;
But when my seven long years are out
        O then I'll marry Sally, –
O then we'll wed, and then we'll bed,
        But not in our alley!

HENRY CAREY

Going to Bed

Come, Madam, come, all rest my powers defie,
Until I labour, I in labour lie.
The foe oft-times having the foe in sight,
Is tir'd with standing though he never fight.
Off with that girdle, like heavens Zone glittering,
But a far fairer world incompassing.
Unpin that spangled breastplate which you wear,
That th'eyes of busie fooles may be stopt there.
Unlace your self, for that harmonious chyme,
Tells me from you, that now it is bed time.
Off with that happy busk, which I envie,
That still can be, and still can stand so nigh.
Your gown going off, such beautious state reveals,
As when from flowry meads th'hills shadow steales.
Off with that wyerie Coronet and shew
The haiery Diademe which on you doth grow:
Now off with those shooes, and then safely tread
In this loves hallow'd temple, this soft bed.
In such white robes, heaven's Angels us'd to be
Receavd by men; Thou Angel bringst with thee
A heaven like Mahomets Paradise; and though
Ill spirits walk in white, we easly know,
But this these Angels from an evil sprite,
Those set our hairs, but these our flesh upright.
　　　　Licence my roaving hands, and let them go,
Before, behind, between, above, below.
O my America! my new-found-land,
My kingdome, safeliest when with one man man'd,
My Myne of precious stones, My Emperie,

How blest am I in this discovering thee!
To enter in these bonds, is to be free;
Then where my hand is set, my seal shall be.
        Full nakedness! All joyes are due to thee,
As souls unbodied, bodies uncloth'd must be,
To taste whole joyes. Gems which you women use
Are like Atlanta's balls, cast in mens views,
That when a fools eye lighteth on a Gem,
His earthly soul may covet theirs, not them.
Like pictures, or like books gay coverings made
For lay-men, are all women thus array'd;
Themselves are mystick books, which only wee
(Whom their imputed grace will dignifie)
Must see reveal'd. Then since that I may know;
As liberally, as to a Midwife, shew
Thy self: cast all, yea, this white lynnen hence,
There is no pennance due to innocence.
        To teach thee, I am naked first; why than
What needst thou have more covering then a man.

JOHN DONNE

Sometimes It Happens

And sometimes it happens that you are friends and then
You are not friends,
And friendship has passed.
And whole days are lost and among them
A fountain empties itself.

And sometimes it happens that you are loved and then
You are not loved,
And love is past.
And whole days are lost and among them
A fountain empties itself into the grass.

And sometimes you want to speak to her and then
You do not want to speak,
Then the opportunity has passed.
Your dreams flare up, they suddenly vanish.

And also it happens that there is nowhere to go and then
There is somewhere to go,
Then you have bypassed.
And the years flare up and are gone,
Quicker than a minute.

So you have nothing.
You wonder if these things matter and then
As soon as you begin to wonder if these things matter
They cease to matter,
And caring is past.
And a fountain empties itself into the grass.

BRIAN PATTEN

Our Lady of the Fiveways

Did you ever see Josie dancing
Where five ways meet,
On a wedge of pavement all on her own
Pistoning at the street?

A V of railings shapes her stage
And iron grey are the bars,
where not-quite-right-in-the-head poor Josie
Dances for the cars.

On and on through the summer night
And traffic roar,
Josie rolls and rocks to a rhythm
You never quite knew before.

For the tune belongs to Josie
And the words are all in her mind.
In her own strange joy and suffering,
Josie makes us kind:

Makes us remember where we are
And the road of love we tread.
Oh, dance on in your dancing heart
For Josie's singing head.

KIT WRIGHT

It Was a Lover and His Lass

It was a lover and his lass
      With a hey and a ho, and a hey-nonino!
That o'er the green cornfield did pass
In the spring time, the only pretty ring time,
When birds do sing hey ding a ding:
      Sweet lovers love the Spring.

Between the acres of the rye
These pretty country folks would lie:
This carol they began that hour,
How that life was but a flower:

And therefore take the present time
      With a hey and a ho and a hey-nonino!
For love is crownèd with the prime
In the spring time, the only pretty ring time,
When birds do sing hey ding a ding:
      Sweet lovers love the Spring.

WILLIAM SHAKESPEARE

I Know Where I'm Going

I know where I'm going,
I know who's going with me,
I know who I love,
But the dear knows who I'll marry.

I'll have stockings of silk,
Shoes of fine green leather,
Combs to buckle my hair
And a ring for every finger.

Feather beds are soft,
Painted rooms are bonny;
But I'd leave them all
To go with my love Johnny.

Some say he's dark,
I say he's bonny,
He's the flower of them all
My handsome, coaxing Johnny.

I know where I'm going,
I know who's going with me,
I know who I love,
But the dear knows who I'll marry.

ANON

The Lover Sheweth How He Is Forsaken of Such As He Sometime Enjoyed

They flee from me, that sometime did me seek,
With naked foot stalking within my chamber:
Once have I seen them gentle, tame and meek,
    That now are wild, and do not once remember,
    That sometime they have put themselves in danger
To take bread at my hand; and now they range
Busily seeking in continual change.

    Thanked be Fortune, it hath been otherwise
Twenty times better; but once especial,
In thin array, after a pleasant guise,
    When her loose gown did from her shoulders fall,
    And she me caught in her arms long and small,
And therewithal so sweetly did me kiss,
And softly said, "Dear heart, how like you this?"

    It was no dream; for I lay broad awaking:
But all is turn'd now through my gentleness,
Into a bitter fashion of forsaking;
    And I have leave to go of her goodness;
    And she also to use new fangleness.
But since that I unkindly so am served:
How like you this, what hath she now deserved?

SIR THOMAS WYATT

Lady 'Rogue' Singleton

Come, wed me, Lady Singleton,
And we will have a baby soon
And we will live in Edmonton
Where all the friendly people run.

I could never make you happy darling,
Or give you the baby you want,
I would always very much rather, dear,
Live in a tent.

I am not a cold woman, Henry,
But I do not feel for you,
What I feel for the elephants and the miasmas
And the general view.

STEVIE SMITH

Jenny Kiss'd Me

Jenny kiss'd me when we met,
    Jumping from the chair she sat in;
Time, you thief, who love to get
    Sweets into your list, put that in!
Say I'm weary, say I'm sad,
    Say that health and wealth have miss'd me,
Say I'm growing old, but add,
    Jenny kiss'd me.

LEIGH HUNT

To His Coy Mistress

Had we but World enough, and Time,
This coyness Lady were no crime.
We would sit down, and think which way
To walk, and pass our long Loves Day.
Thou by the *Indian Ganges* side
Should'st Rubies find: I by the Tide
Of *Humber* would complain. I would
Love you ten years before the Flood:
And you should if you please refuse
Till the Conversion of the *Jews*.
My vegetable Love should grow
Vaster than Empires, and more slow.
An hundred years should go to praise
Thine Eyes, and on thy Forehead Gaze.
Two hundred to adore each Breast:
But thirty thousand to the rest.
An Age at least to every part,
And the last Age should show your Heart.
For Lady you deserve this State;
Nor would I love at lower rate.
        But at my back I alwaies hear
Times winged Charriot hurrying near:
And yonder all before us lye
Desarts of vast Eternity.
Thy Beauty shall no more be found;
Nor, in thy marble Vault, shall sound
My ecchoing Song: then Worms shall try
That long preserv'd Virginity:
And your quaint Honour turn to dust;

And into ashes all my Lust.
The Grave's a fine and private place,
But none I think do there embrace.
        Now therefore, while the youthful hew
Sits on thy skin like morning dew,
And while thy willing Soul transpires
At every pore with instant Fires,
Now let us sport us while we may;
And now, like am'rous birds of prey,
Rather at once our Time devour,
Than languish in his slow-chapt pow'r.
Let us roll all our Strength, and all
Our sweetness, up into one Ball:
And tear our Pleasures with rough strife,
Thorough the Iron gates of Life.
Thus, though we cannot make our Sun
Stand still, yet we will make him run.

ANDREW MARVELL

I Knew a Woman

I knew a woman, lovely in her bones,
When small birds sighed, she would sigh back at them;
Ah, when she moved, she moved more ways than one:
The shapes a bright container can contain!
Of her choice virtues only gods should speak
Or English poets who grew up on Greek
(I'd have them sing in chorus, cheek to cheek).

How well her wishes went! She stroked my chin,
She taught me Turn, and Counter-turn, and Stand;
She taught me Touch, that undulant white skin;
I nibbled meekly from her proffered hand;
She was the sickle; I, poor I, the rake
Coming behind her for her pretty sake
(But what prodigious mowing we did make).

Love likes a gander, and adores a goose:
Her full lips pursed, the errant note to seize;
She played it quick, she played it light and loose;
My eyes, they dazzled at her flowing knees;
Her several parts could keep a pure repose,
Or one hip quiver with a mobile nose
(She moved in circles, and those circles moved).

Let seed be grass, and grass turn into hay:
I'm martyr to a motion not my own;
What's freedom for? To know eternity.
I swear she cast a shadow white as stone.
But who would count eternity in days?

These old bones live to learn her wanton ways:
(I measure time by how a body sways).

THEODORE ROETHKE

Guilty

Yes, baby, I been drinkin'
And I shouldn't come by I know
But I found myself in trouble
And I had nowhere else to go

Got some whisky from the barman
Got some cocaine from a friend
I just had to keep on movin'
Till I was back in your arms again

Guilty, baby, I'm guilty
And I'll be guilty all the rest of my life
How come I never do what I'm supposed to do
How come nothin' that I try to do ever turns out right?

You know, you know how it is with me, baby,
You know, I just can't stand myself
And it takes a whole lot of medicine
For me to pretend that I'm someone else

RANDY NEWMAN

Fantasia on a Line of Stefan George

I shall die if I do not touch your body.
If I cannot claim a small priest-like
Privilege at your waist, my masks
Of face will slip, no tides will work
Your body's shores, no storms rouse
That inland sea. On a hectoring day
I stood in the Natural History Museum
And couldn't breathe. The blue whale
And the passenger pigeon worried for me,
Surely my fingers were losing their prints,
I had no history in my bones, I was
Transparent as a finished gesture.
Where you are is life: this sunlessness
Is only inside my head,
The inverse paradise, rain forest where
Evolution's mother blocked with eggs
Waddles with beak aloft to spin
The thread of fear that leads back to you.

PETER PORTER

To My Dear and Loving Husband

If ever two were one, then surely we.
If ever man were loved by wife, then thee;
If ever wife was happy in a man,
Compare with me, ye women, if you can.
I prize thy love more than whole mines of gold,
Or all the riches that the East doth hold.
My love is such that rivers cannot quench,
Nor aught but love from thee give recompense.
Thy love is such I can no way repay;
The heavens reward thee manifold, I pray.
Then while we live, in love let's so persever,
That when we live no more we may live ever.

ANNE BRADSTREET

Naked Out of the Dark

Naked out of the dark we came.
Naked into the dark we go.
Come to my arms, naked in the dark.

KENNETH REXROTH

The Armada

Long long ago
when everything I was told was believable
and the little I knew was less limited than now,
I stretched belly down on the grass beside a pond
and to the far bank launched a child's armada.

A broken fortress of twigs,
the paper-tissue sails of galleons,
the waterlogged branches of submarines –
all came to ruin and were on flame
in that dusk-red pond.
And you, mother, stood behind me,
impatient to be going,
old at twenty-three, alone,
thin overcoat flapping.

How closely the past shadows us.
In a hospital a mile or so from that pond
I kneel beside your bed and, closing my eyes,
reach out across forty years to touch once more
that pond's cool surface,
and it is your cool skin I'm touching;
for as on a pond a child's paper boat
was blown out of reach
by the smallest gust of wind,
so too have you been blown out of reach
by the smallest whisper of death,
and a childhood memory is sharpened,
and the heart burns as that armada burnt,
long, long ago.

BRIAN PATTEN

Atlas

There is a kind of love called maintenance,
Which stores the WD40 and knows when to use it;

Which checks the insurance, and doesn't forget
The milkman; which remembers to plant bulbs;

Which answers letters; which knows the way
The money goes; which deals with dentists

And Road Fund Tax and meeting trains,
And postcards to the lonely; which upholds

The permanently ricketty elaborate
Structures of living; which is Atlas.

And maintenance is the sensible side of love,
Which knows what time and weather are doing
To my brickwork; insulates my faulty wiring;
Laughs at my dryrotten jokes; remembers
My need for gloss and grouting; which keeps
My suspect edifice upright in air,
As Atlas did the sky.

U. A. FANTHORPE

In May

In a nook
That opened south
you and I
Lay mouth to mouth.

A snowy gull
And sooty daw
Came and looked
With many a caw;

"Such," I said,
"Are I and you,
When you've kissed me
Black and blue!"

J. M. SYNGE

THE PARTY'S OVER

on your way, then – thanks for coming,
oh, and here – take a few extra for luck
and I hope you invite me
to a party of your poems some day.

To Be Carved on Gravestones

For Himself

I was buried near this dyke,
That my friends may weep as much as they like.

WILLIAM BLAKE

For Elizabeth Ireland

Here I lie at the chancel door,
Here I lie because I'm poor:
The further in, the more you pay:
Here lie I as warm as they.

For Anon

Here lies I, no wonder I'm dead,
For a broad-wheel'd wagon went over my head.

For Johnny Doo

Wha lies here?
I, Johnny Doo.
Hoo, Johnny, is that you?
Ay, man, but a'm dead noo.

For a Golden Retriever

It was my job
To be a dog.
My master said
That I was good.
Now I turn myself around
And lie down in the musty ground.

ADRIAN MITCHELL

For Himself
My Own Epitaph

Life is a jest, and all things show it,
I thought so once; but now I know it.

JOHN GAY

For Martin Elginbrod

Here lie I, Martin Elginbrod.
Hae mercy on my soul, Lord God;
As I would do, were I Lord God,
And ye were Martin Elginbrod.

For Lord Castlereagh

Posterity will ne'er survey
     A nobler grave than this:
Here lie the bones of Castlereagh:
     Stop, traveller, and piss.

GEORGE GORDON, LORD BYRON

Upon the Death of Sir Albert Morton's Wife

He first deceased; she for a little tried
To live without him, liked it not, and died.

SIR HENRY WOOTON

Fidele

Fear no more the heat o' the sun
      Nor the furious winter's rages;
Thou thy worldly task hast done,
      Home art gone and ta'en thy wages:
Golden lads and girls all must,
As chimney-sweepers, come to dust.

Fear no more the frown o' the great,
      Thou art past the tyrant's stroke:
Care no more to clothe and eat;
      To thee the reed is as the oak:
The sceptre, learning, physic, must
All follow this, and come to dust.

Fear no more the lightning-flash
      Nor the all-dreaded thunder-stone;
Fear not slander, censure rash;
      Thou hast finish'd joy and moan:
All lovers young, all lovers must
Consign to thee and come to dust.

WILLIAM SHAKESPEARE

Apple Blossom

The first blossom was the best blossom
For the child who never had seen an orchard;
For the youth whom whisky had led astray
The morning after was the first day.

The first apple was the best apple
For Adam before he heard the sentence;
When the flaming sword endorsed the Fall
The trees were his to plant for all.

The first ocean was the best ocean
For the child from streets of doubt and litter;
For the youth for whom the skies unfurled
His first love was his first world.

But the first verdict seemed the worst verdict
When Adam and Eve were expelled from Eden;
Yet when the bitter gates clanged to
The sky beyond was just as blue.

For the next ocean is the first ocean
And the last ocean is the first ocean
And, however often the sun may rise,
A new thing dawns upon our eyes.

For the last blossom is the first blossom
And the first blossom is the best blossom
And when from Eden we take our way
The morning after is the first day.

LOUIS MACNEICE

from The Proverbs of Hell

Drive your cart and your plough over the bones of the dead.
    The road of excess leads to the palace of wisdom.
The cut worm forgives the plough.
    A fool sees not the same tree that a wise man sees.
No bird soars too high, if he soars with his own wings.
    The most sublime act is to set another before you.
If the fool would persist in his folly he would become wise.
    Prisons are built with stones of Law, brothels with bricks
        of Religion.

    The pride of the peacock is the glory of God.
    The lust of the goat is the bounty of God.
    The wrath of the lion is the wisdom of God.
    The nakedness of woman is the work of God.

The bird a nest, the spider a web, man friendship.
    What is now proved was once only imagin'd.
The cistern contains; the fountain overflows.
    One thought fills immensity.
The tigers of wrath are wiser than the horses of instruction.
    Listen to the fool's reproach! It is a kingly title!
The soul of sweet delight can never be defil'd.
    When thou seest an eagle, thou seest a portion of Genius;
    lift up thy head!
To create a little flower is the labour of ages.
    Damn braces. Bless relaxes.

The head Sublime,
The heart Pathos,
The genitals Beauty,
The hands and feet Proportion.

Exuberance is Beauty.
　　Enough! or Too much.

WILLIAM BLAKE

from Jerusalem

I give you the end of a golden string;
　　Only wind it into a ball,
It will lead you in at Heaven's gate,
　　Built in Jerusalem's wall.

The fields from Islington to Marybone,
　　To Primrose Hill and Saint John's Wood,
Were builded over with pillars of gold;
　　And there Jerusalem's pillars stood.

Her Little Ones ran on the fields,
　　The Lamb of God among them seen,
And fair Jerusalem, His Bride,
　　Among the little meadows green.

Pancras and Kentish Town repose
　　Among her golden pillars high,

Among her golden arches which
    Shine upon the starry sky.

The Jew's-harp House and the Green Man,
    The Ponds where boys to bathe delight,
The fields of cows by Willan's farm,
    Shine in Jerusalem's pleasant sight…

In my Exchanges every land
    Shall walk; and mine in every land,
Mutual shall build Jerusalem,
    Both heart in heart and hand in hand.

WILLIAM BLAKE

Blue Suede Shoes

Well, it's one for the money,
Two for the show,
Three to get ready, now
Go, cat, go!
But don't you step on my blue suede shoes.
You can do anything, but lay off of my blue suede shoes.

Well you can knock me down,
Step in my face,
Slander my name
All over the place;
Do anything
You want to do,
But uh-uh, honey lay off of my shoes
Don't you step on my blue suede shoes.

Burn my house,
Steal my car,
Drink my liquor
From an old fruit jar.
Do anything
You want to do,
But uh-uh, honey lay off of my shoes
Don't you step on my blue suede shoes.

You can do anything but lay off of my blue suede shoes.

CARL LEE PERKINS

THE LIVING END

Acknowledgements

'Against Coupling' by Fleur Adcock from SELECTED POEMS published by Oxford University Press in 1983, reprinted by permission of Oxford University Press; 'Dog Show', words and music by Laurie Anderson © Difficult Music/BMG Music Publishing Ltd. All rights reserved. Used by permission; 'Faded Glamour' and 'Near the Moon' by Hugh Barker, lyrics used by permission of the author; 'The Promised Land' by Chuck Berry. Used by permission; 'Leaps of Feeling' by James Berry from WHEN I DANCE, reprinted by permission of The Peters Fraser and Dunlop Group Limited on behalf of James Berry. 'Looking Up' by Sujata Bhatt, © Sujata Bhatt. Used by permission of the author; 'Muliebrity' by Sujata Bhatt from BRUNIZEM, reprinted by permission of Carcanet Press Limited; 'Concerning the Infanticide, Marie Farrar' by Bertholt Brecht translated by H. R. Hays, from SELECTED POEMS, © H. R. Hays, reprinted by permission of Ann Elmo Agency, Inc.; 'Solstice Roundelay' by Jeff Cloves is printed by permission of Jeff Cloves. 'Advert' and 'History Never Happened' © Mr Social Control. Used by permission of the author; 'Foreign' by Carol Ann Duffy is taken from SELLING MANHATTAN, published by Anvil Press Poetry in 1987. 'Queen Kong' by Carol Ann Duffy is printed by permission of the author; 'Subterranean Homesick Blues' by Bob Dylan, © 1965 by Warner Bros. Music, copyright renewed 1993 by Special Rider Music. All rights reserved. International copyright secured. Reprinted by permission; 'Collateral Damage' and 'Atlas' © U. A. Fanthorpe (Peterloo Poets, 1995) Reproduced by permission. 'What Happens' © Erich Fried from 100 POEMS WITHOUT A COUNTRY, translated by Stuart Hood published by Calder Publications. Used by permission of the Calder Educational Trust; 'Ray's Workshop' © Cicely Herbert, first published in The New Statesman. Reprinted by permission of the author; 'Mooses' by Ted Hughes from UNDER THE NORTH STAR, 'How Water Began to Play' by Ted Hughes from CROW and 'Full Moon and Little Frieda' by Ted Hughes from WODWO all published by Faber & Faber Ltd. Used by permission; 'The Preacher Tells a Story by the Graveside' by Henrik Ibsen from Peer Gynt. Adrian Mitchell's adaptation of Karin Bamborough's translation. Used by permission; 'The Visit' by Judith Kazantzis, copyright and acknowledgements to the author 1995, 1997, 1999. Acknowledgements for first publication 1995 The New Statesman and Society, and to Enitharmon Press 1997 for Judith Kazantis' poetry collection SWIMMING THROUGH THE GRAND HOTEL in which this poem is included; 'The Mosquito Knows' by D. H. Lawrence from THE COMPLETE POEMS OF D. H. LAWRENCE. Reprinted by permission of Laurence Pollinger Limited and the Estate of Frieda Lawrence Ravagli; 'Riot in Cell Block Number Nine' by Jerry Leiber and Mike Stoller, © 1954 (Renewed) Jerry Leiber Music, Mike Stoller Music. All rights reserved. Used by permission; 'Stagger Lee' by Harold Logan and Lloyd Price. Used by permission; 'Apple Blossom' by Louis MacNeice from COLLECTED POEMS, published by Faber & Faber Ltd. Used by permission; 'The Lake' by Roger McGough from HOLIDAY ON DEATH ROW. Reprinted with permission of The Peters Fraser and Dunlop Group Limited on behalf of Roger McGough; 'Dinner Tickets', 'Velvet Wave', 'Trouble Is', and 'Day With George' by Paul McCartney © 1994 Paul McCartney. Used by permission; 'Jake's Amazing Suit' and 'One Bad Word' by Adrian Mitchell from HEART ON THE LEFT published by Bloodaxe Books, 'Third Time Unlucky' by Adrian Mitchell from BALLOON LAGOON published by Orchard Books, and 'A Puppy Called

Puberty' by Adrian Mitchell from BLUE COFFEE published by Bloodaxe Books; 'Frontier Story' and 'Blue Toboggans' by Edwin Morgan from COLLECTED POEMS, FROM GLASGOW TO SATURN, published by Carcanet Press Limited; 'Ode to the Tomato' by Pablo Neruda translated by Nathaniel Tarn from SELECTED POEMS edited by Nathaniel Tarn, published by Jonathan Cape; 'Birmingham' and 'Guilty' by Randy Newman ('Birmingham' from the album 'Good Old Boys', Warner Brothers). Used by permission; 'For Forest' by Grace Nichols from LAZY THOUGHTS OF A LAZY WOMAN, published by Virago Press; 'Moggy at Grimma's' by Dorothy Nimmo from THE CHILDREN'S GAME published by Smith Doorstop 1998, reprinted by permission of the author; 'Do the Dead Know What Time It Is?' by Kenneth Patchen, from COLLECTED POEMS published by New Directions. Used by permission; 'Inattention', 'The Minister of Exams' and 'The Armada' from ARMADA; 'Sometimes it Happens' from LITTLE JOHNNY'S CONFESSION, by Brian Patten, published by HarperCollins Ltd.; 'God Bless the Poor' © Brian Patten, c/o Puffin Books, London; 'Blue Suede Shoes' words and music by Carl Lee Perkins © 1956 by Hi-Lo Music, Inc. Public performance rights for USA and Canada controlled by Hi-Lo Music, Inc., a BMI affiliate. All other rights for the world controlled by Unichappell Music, Inc. (Rightsong Music, publisher). All Rights Reserved. Used by kind permission of Carlin Music Corp., Iron Bridge House, 3 Bridge Approach, Chalk Farm, London NW1 8BD; 'Fantasia on a Line of Stefan George' by Peter Porter from COLLECTED POEMS, published by Oxford University Press 1983. Reprinted by permission of Oxford University Press; 'Blue Suede Shoes' by Carl Lee Perkins. Used by permission; 'From the Persian' by Kenneth Rexroth from COLLECTED SHORTER POEMS, published by New Directions. Used by permission; 'The Waking' and 'I Knew a Woman' by Theodore Roethke from COLLECTED POEMS published by Faber & Faber Ltd. Used by permission; 'Massacre of the Boys' by Tadeusz Rozewicz and translated by Adam Czerniawski is taken from THEY CAME TO SEE A POET published by Anvil Press Poetry in 1991; 'Freedom to Dream' by Andrew Salkey, reprinted with kind permission of Patricia Salkey; 'Robinson Crusoe' and 'The Great Staircase' by Eric Satie, translated by Beatrix M. Craig and Adrian Mitchell. Used by permission; 'Lady "Rogue" Singleton' by Stevie Smith from THE COLLECTED POEMS OF STEVIE SMITH. Used by permission of James MacGibbon; 'I'm a Rocker' Bruce Springsteen. Used by permission; 'How to make a chandelier' and 'East St O'Neal' © Hank Starrs, lyrics used by permission of the author; 'A Glass of Beer' by James Stephens from COLLECTED POEMS. Used by permission of The Society of Authors as the Literary Representative of the Estate of James Stephens; 'Dancing in the Street' by William Stevenson, Marvin Gaye and Ivy Hunter. Used by permission; 'Low Down Dirty Shame Blues' by Joe Turner, lyrics used by kind permission of MCA Music Ltd © 1940; 'Villon's Straight Tip to All Cross Coves' by François Villon was translated by W.E.Henley; 'The Ballad of Villon and Fat Madge' by François Villon was translated by Algernon Swinburne; Extract from 'Jambo' © Dave Ward, published by Impact Books 1992. Used by permission of the author; 'Our Lady of the Fiveways' by Kit Wright, © Kit Wright. Used by permission of the author.

While every effort has been made to obtain permissions, we apologise for any omissions.

Index of Poets

Index of First Lines

spare
corkscrew